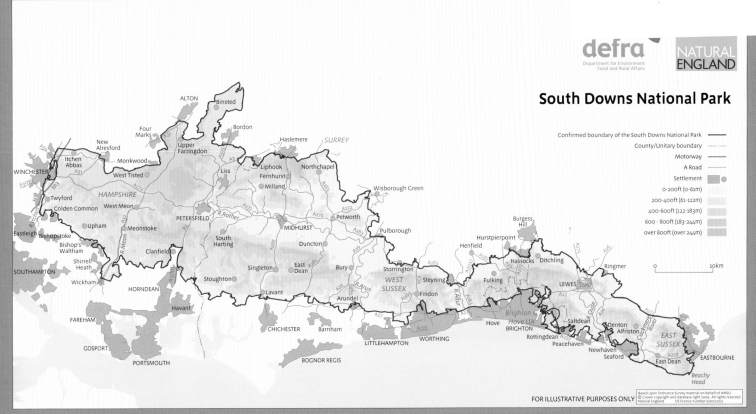

The South Downs National Park showing the Park boundary, major towns and villages, rivers and main roads. Note how in the east, the north–south flowing rivers cut through South Downs to the sea, whilst in the west drainage is dominated by the west–east flowing Rother that captures all drainage from the north until it joins the southward flowing Arun near Pulborough. (Reproduced by courtesy of Natural England.)

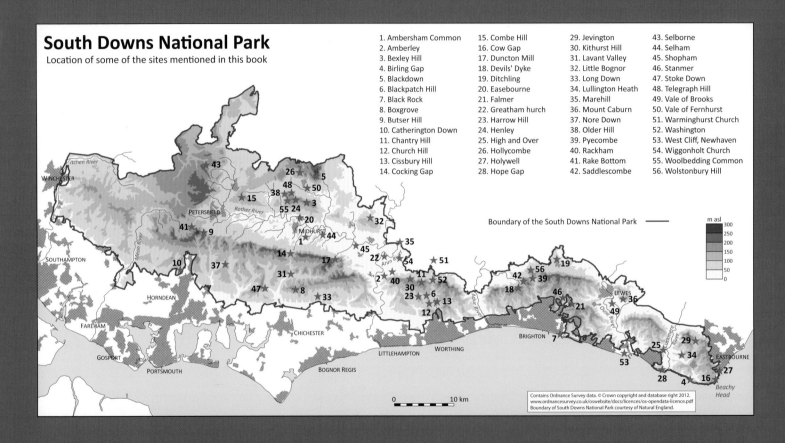

South Downs National Park

Location of some of the sites mentioned in this book

1. Ambersham Common
2. Amberley
3. Bexley Hill
4. Birling Gap
5. Blackdown
6. Blackpatch Hill
7. Black Rock
8. Boxgrove
9. Butser Hill
10. Catherington Down
11. Chantry Hill
12. Church Hill
13. Cissbury Hill
14. Cocking Gap

15. Combe Hill
16. Cow Gap
17. Duncton Mill
18. Devils' Dyke
19. Ditchling
20. Easebourne
21. Falmer
22. Greatham hurch
23. Harrow Hill
24. Henley
25. High and Over
26. Hollycombe
27. Holywell
28. Hope Gap

29. Jevington
30. Kithurst Hill
31. Lavant Valley
32. Little Bognor
33. Long Down
34. Lullington Heath
35. Marehill
36. Mount Caburn
37. Nore Down
38. Older Hill
39. Pyecombe
40. Rackham
41. Rake Bottom
42. Saddlescombe

43. Selborne
44. Selham
45. Shopham
46. Stanmer
47. Stoke Down
48. Telegraph Hill
49. Vale of Brooks
50. Vale of Fernhurst
51. Warminghurst Church
52. Washington
53. West Cliff, Newhaven
54. Wiggonholt Church
55. Woolbedding Common
56. Wolstonbury Hill

Boundary of the South Downs National Park ——

m asl
300
250
200
150
100
50
0

Contains Ordnance Survey data. © Crown copyright and database right 2012.
www.ordnancesurvey.co.uk/oswebsite/docs/licences/os-opendata-licence.pdf
Boundary of South Downs National Park courtesy of Natural England.

0   10 km

The Geology and Scenery of the South Downs National Park

by David Robinson

ISBN 978-0-904973-24-2

Published by The Sussex Archaeological Society, Lewes

Designed and typeset by Dora A. Kemp, MPhil

Printed in Great Britain by Short Run Press, Exeter

Contents

© Airscapes.co.uk

The Chalk scarp west of Devil's Dyke.

The Geology and Scenery of the South Downs National Park

Acknowledgements

This book is based on study and research into the geology, landforms and scenery of southeast England and in particular the area now designated as the South Downs National Park, by many people over many years. It is an area that I have come to love and know well since taking up a post in physical geography at the University of Sussex over forty years ago. I am pleased to have been given the opportunity to share my knowledge and understanding of the geology and scenery of this wonderful landscape by the Sussex Archaeological Society, and their sponsors, in this small book. However, it could not have been written and so beautifully illustrated without the help of a number of people to whom I am greatly indebted. First, for help with the illustrative materials I would like to thank Peter Anderton and the RIGS team at the Biological Records Centre, Woods Mill, Henfield, most notably Henri Brocklebank, who gave me access to a rich source of photographs and assisted with their editing. Further photographs were kindly provided by one of my regular walking companions for many years, Ben du Boulay. Aerial photographs were taken specially to illustrate this, and other books in the series, by Russ Oliver at Airscapes. I also wish to thank Martin Eade, John Manley, Geoffrey Mead and Tony Wilson for permission to include their photographs. All photographs not otherwise acknowledged are mine. The geology map was prepared and kindly made available by Chris Manning and the South Downs National Park Authority. The text has been improved, and errors reduced by David Bone, John Cooper, Rendel Williams, John Manley and Robin Milner-Gulland, who kindly read and commented on earlier drafts. David, with his encyclopedic knowledge of West Sussex and adjacent parts of Hampshire, was particularly helpful in his comments on those parts of the National Park I know less well. Any remaining errors or faults are my responsibility alone.

Given size limitations, the book can only be an introduction to the geology and scenery of the National Park. For those wishing to advance their knowledge further some suggestions for additional reading are provided at the end of the book.

(Left) General view of the South Downs showing the steep north-facing scarp slope and the more gently sloping southern slope descending towards Brighton. The scarp here is heavily wooded and indented by short scarp face valleys called coombs.

The town of Lewes lying in the gap cut through the Chalk by the River Ouse. The eastern Downs are divided into distinct blocks by the large valleys of southward-flowing rivers that drain the land to the north.

The Geology and Scenery of the South Downs National Park

Introduction

The South Downs National Park (henceforth the Park) is named after the bold rounded hills that run across East and West Sussex from the coast at Eastbourne in the east, into Hampshire in the west. Composed throughout of a soft porous limestone known as Chalk, the hills are characterized by a steep generally northward-facing scarp slope and a more gently inclined, southerly dip slope dissected by valley systems, most of which no longer contain active stream flow even in wet winter weather. Standing on the crest of the Downs, the scarp below is the soil and vegetation covered face of the thick beds of Chalk rock that once continued to rise northwards over central Sussex, forming the cap of an elongated, uplifted dome aligned generally west-northwest to east-southeast, that stretches from Hampshire eastwards across Sussex and Kent and then across what today is the English Channel into northern France. Since this dome was formed, erosion has breached the Chalk cap to expose the older rocks

that lie beneath. On a clear day, looking north from the crest of the South Downs between Lewes and the Adur river gap at Bramber, one can look across the entire outcrop of these older rocks, which form an area of varied relief known as the Weald, to the North Downs of Surrey and Kent, where the Chalk cap survives, dipping away on the north side of the dome. In the west, in Hampshire, the dome dies away, the rocks were never uplifted to the same extent and erosion has not yet breached the Chalk cap. As a consequence, west of Petersfield, the steep scarp slope curves northwards and then northeast, in the form of a great horseshoe, to link up with the North Downs beyond the boundary of the Park in Surrey. In the east the boundary of the Park mostly lies close to the foot of the scarp of the Downs, but west of the river Arun the boundary lies further north and includes a large area of the underlying older rocks of the Western Weald. This is a region of varied topography developed on clays and sands, including strong sandstones that create areas of high ground, which limits the distance north that can be viewed from the top of the Chalk scarp.

Looking south from central Sussex, the continuity of the impressive crest of the South Downs is broken by the wide deep valleys of the south flowing Arun, Adur, Ouse and Cuckmere rivers. The flat, alluvial floors of these valleys lie only a little above present-day sea-level and this divides the eastern Downs into five distinct blocks. West of the Arun, no river valleys cut through the scarp and the continuity of the crest of the Downs is more complete, although its height is lowered in places where the heads of major dry valleys lower the crest to form 'wind gaps', the most notable of which lies south of Cocking. The crest of the Chalk blocks further east is lowered by similar gaps at Washington, Saddlescombe, Pyecombe, Clayton and Jevington.

In West Sussex and Hampshire, the southerly dipping Chalk disappears rather imperceptibly along the southern boundary of the Park under a cover of younger sands and clays that underlie the Sussex Coastal Plain and the eastern margins of the Hampshire Basin. By contrast, in East Sussex, the Chalk is terminated abruptly by the sea and forms magnificent cliffs that run for some 27 km

© Peter Anderton (RIGS/SBRC)

The rocks and their origins

In geological terms, the Park is underlain by relatively young sedimentary rocks. They range in age from the geological period known as the Cretaceous through the Palaeogene and Neogene to the Quaternary. The oldest rocks today exposed at the ground surface are formed of sediments deposited approximately 133 million years ago. Deposition occurred almost continuously from this date for 55–60 million years with only short periods when erosion intervened. Conditions of deposition occurred under a variety of environmental conditions in which clays and sands were initially dominant before the region was inundated by an expanding sea in which the soft, pure, limestone known as Chalk was laid down. The region then began to be uplifted to become a low-lying, domed land mass subject to erosion, before a further inundation occurred around 59 million years ago, which probably lasted for between 5 and 10 million years in the area of the Park. During this period, further deposits, mostly sands and clays were deposited before renewed uplift occurred and since then

The lowered crest of the Chalk scarp south of Cocking. An example of high-level 'wind gap' where the crest of the Chalk scarp is lowered many tens of metres. These gaps are believed to be the routes of past rivers flowing south before the land to the north was lowered by erosion and drainage diverted east along the Rother.

from Brighton to Eastbourne, reaching over 150 m in height at Beachy Head and interrupted only by the estuaries of the Ouse and Cuckmere rivers. In places, the southerly dipping Chalk is overlain by a variety of mostly thin, superficial geological deposits. The cover of these superficial deposits generally increases westwards and they are particularly widespread on parts of the Hampshire Downs. This results in a more varied pattern of soils and a greater variety of natural flora and land use than would prevail on the Chalk alone.

the rocks have been exposed to weathering and erosion under a variety of differing climates. The most dramatic of the climatic variations, in terms of their influence on the present-day landscape, have been the oscillating climates of the last 2.6 million years, in the period known as the Quaternary, when the region suffered repeated periods of intensely cold periglacial climate, during which the ground was permanently frozen to great depth, and intervening periods when the climate was as warm, or sometimes warmer, than the present day.

During deposition the older sediments were buried by successively younger deposits and in consequence as these consolidated to form rock, a process known as lithification, the younger rocks overlay the older. When they were subsequently uplifted to form a land mass, uplift was greatest along a line that runs approximately WNW–ESE across central Sussex. Lying south of this line of maximum uplift, most of the rocks within the Park dip regionally to the south. Subsequent erosion of the younger rocks has been greatest where the uplift was greatest, and it is here that the oldest rocks are now exposed. Traversing south, progressively younger, overlying rocks outcrop at the surface. Exceptionally,

Era	Period	Epoch	Age Ma	Park
CENOZOIC (TERTIARY)	QUATERNARY	Holocene	0.012	
		Pleistocene	2.6	
	NEOGENE	Pliocene	5.3	
		Miocene	23	
	PALAEOGENE	Oligocene	34	
		Eocene	56	
		Palaeocene	66	
MESOZOIC	CRETACEOUS	Upper Cretaceous	100	
		Lower Cretaceous	145	

Names and time divisions of the geology of the National Park. Sediments that became rocks were deposited within at least parts of the Park during those periods shaded grey in the right-hand column. During the unshaded periods marked with a cross the Park was subject to erosion and no rock-forming sediments were deposited. Ma = millions of years ago.

Modified after a version by Peter Anderton (RIGS/SBRC)

© Ben du Boulay

In East Sussex the Chalk is terminated along the coast by impressive cliffs.

Epoch	Age Ma	Rock units
Holocene	0.012	local
Pleistocene	2.6	local
Pliocene Miocene Oligocene U Eocene		Missing due to erosion
	41	
Eocene		Bracklesham Group
		Thames Group (London Clay)
Palaeocene	59	Lambeth Group
Upper Cretaceous		Missing due to erosion
	72	
		White Chalk
	94	
	100	Grey Chalk
Lower Cretaceous		Upper Greensand
	113	Gault Clay
		Lower Greensand
	125	
	133	Weald Clay

Modified after a version by Peter Anderton (RIGS/SBRC)

The sequence of rocks that occur in the National Park. The youngest rock of widespread occurrence is the Chalk, rocks younger than this occur only in small areas, mostly near the southern margins or as re-worked material overlying the Chalk.

towards the northern boundary of the Park in northwest Sussex, approaching the Surrey border, the rocks lie north of the line of maximum uplift and dip gently northwards. Approaching Hampshire, uplift was much less and most of the younger rocks have not yet been removed by erosion. In consequence, the western parts of the Park are mostly underlain by Chalk or younger rocks. The rocks younger than the Chalk were formed after the doming of the region and are not tilted in the same way. The thin and patchy Quaternary deposits were laid down long after much of the erosion of the region had occurred and lie scattered across the eroded surface of the earlier rocks.

The Wealden group: the Weald Clay

The oldest rocks sculptured by erosion to form the surface of the Park are those lying north and west of the South Downs in West Sussex. The oldest are poor draining, mudstones and clays, known collectively as the Weald Clay, which today floor the low ground of the Vale of Fernhurst and adjacent areas of the Low Weald. These deposits were laid down in shallow water on what is believed to have been a vast, alluvial floodplain over a period of 12–14 million years, commencing approximately

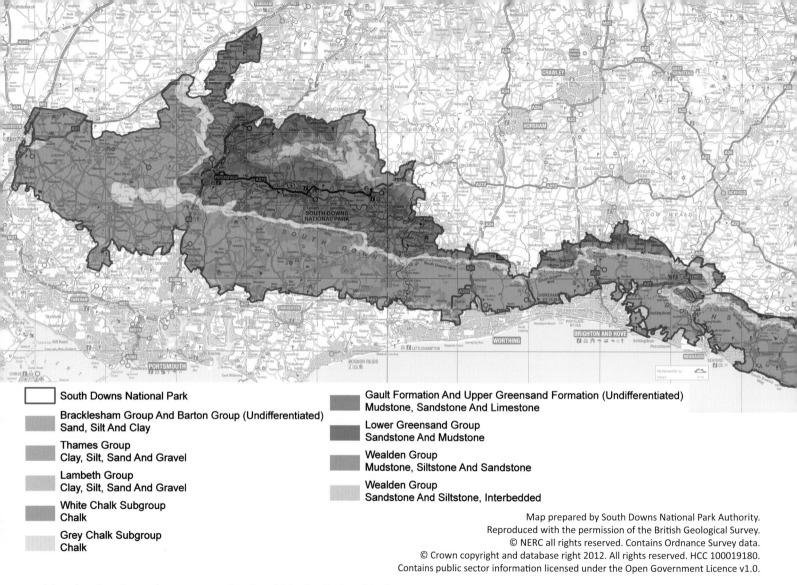

South Downs National Park

Bracklesham Group And Barton Group (Undifferentiated)
Sand, Silt And Clay

Thames Group
Clay, Silt, Sand And Gravel

Lambeth Group
Clay, Silt, Sand And Gravel

White Chalk Subgroup
Chalk

Grey Chalk Subgroup
Chalk

Gault Formation And Upper Greensand Formation (Undifferentiated)
Mudstone, Sandstone And Limestone

Lower Greensand Group
Sandstone And Mudstone

Wealden Group
Mudstone, Siltstone And Sandstone

Wealden Group
Sandstone And Siltstone, Interbedded

Map showing the surface outcrop of rocks within the National Park.

The Western Weald from Henley showing the wooded nature of the low countryside of the Vale of Fernhurst, which is underlain predominantly by the Weald Clay, overlooked in the distance by steep slopes developed in sandstones of the Hythe Formation.

© Ben du Boulay

© Ben du Boulay

© David Robinson

Wiggonholt Church is one of many buildings within the Park with a roof of Horsham Stone (see detail above), a thinly bedded sandstone that occurs within the Weald Clay.

130 million years ago. Although the sediments deposited on this plain were predominantly muddy, there were short periods when sedimentation was dominated by coarser sand, resulting in the formation of predominantly thinly bedded, flaggy sandstones, some of which show fossil ripple marks similar to those you can see at low tide on some beaches at the present day. The most famous of these thin sandstones is 'Horsham Stone', which attains a maximum thickness of approximately 10 m. Although quarried only at locations outside the Park, this stone was widely used throughout West Sussex for roofing and paving slabs, including for houses and churches within the Park. The sandstones never stand free of a soil cover, but they do give rise to some short steep slopes in the otherwise flattish countryside.

The Weald Clay also contains several thin limestone bands, some of which contain masses of shells of a freshwater snail called

The massed shells of *Viviparus* a freshwater snail are clearly visible in freshly broken surfaces of 'Paludina Limestone' or 'Winklestone'. The stone can be polished and was used as a decorative stone known as 'Sussex' or 'Petworth' Marble.

When exposed to the weather, 'Paludina Limestone' disintegrates badly as can be seen from this stone in the wall of Warminghurst Church.

A floor slab of 'Paludina Limestone' in Greatham Church. Originally this single slab was probably a decorative altar slab that was removed and relocated during the Reformation.

Viviparus. This snail was formerly known as *Paludina*, and the limestones sometimes as 'Paludina Limestone' or 'Winklestone'. Cut surfaces can be polished and the limestone was quarried as 'Petworth' or 'Sussex' Marble. In the vicinity of the Park it was quarried around Kirdford and Plaistow, and although no quarries remain, good exam-ples of the use of the 'marble' for decorative stonework can be found in several localities within the Park, including chimney pieces in Petworth House and fine fonts in churches such as those in Parham Park and Trotton. Elsewhere, outside the Park, examples of its use can be found in Chichester and Canterbury Cathedrals and Westminster Abbey. It was used also for altar slabs, internal flooring and occasionally for external work, such as flagstones in churchyards, but it does not survive well when exposed to the weather.

A further resource extracted from the Weald Clay around Fernhurst was iron ore for the Wealden Iron industry that flourished in

The sandstones in the Hythe Formation show considerable variation in thickness and cementation as can be seen from these two examples. *(Left)* A massive block from a bed over 3 m in thickness at Codmore Hill. *(Right)* Sandstone beds less than about 0.5 m thick interbedded with weaker beds of sand at Older Hill.

the 13th to as late as the 18th century. The ore occurs within the clay as layers of large concretionary nodules, called 'doggers', and tabular masses of siderite, an iron carbonate. It was dug from circular pits and the remnants of these, comprising areas of uneven ground with small circular ponds, or areas of boggy ground surrounded by raised rims of spoil, still survive in some woodlands with descriptive names such as Minepit Copse and Furnace Wood.

The Lower Greensand Group

The Weald Clay is overlain by a further band of clay known as the Atherfield Clay. In contrast to the predominantly grey colour of the Weald Clay, this clay tends to be chocolate brown and the fossils it contains indicate the arrival of marine conditions. Encroaching from the west, this sea eroded the top of the Weald Clay slightly before the Atherfield Clay was deposited and there is a sharp junction between the two clays. Deposition of clay was short-lived and sandy sediment soon began to be deposited. In consequence the Atherfield Clay is only a few metres thick and thins eastwards to less than a metre before disappearing completely. Within the Park, the Atherfield Clay outcrops towards the base of the steep escarpment of the Hythe Formation, where it is mostly obscured by debris from the slopes above and is only rarely exposed in temporary road and ditch cuttings.

The Atherfield Clay grades upwards into a sequence of sandy deposits which, together with the Atherfield Clay are known jointly as the Lower Greensand. The first of these sandy deposits is the Hythe Formation which, within the Park boundary, comprises sands, loams and sandstones with subordinate, often lens-shaped, masses of chert. They are thickest in the northwest, where they exceed 60 m in thickness, and thin southwards and eastwards, especially east of Midhurst. The sandy layers are loose and friable but the sandstone layers are cemented to form massive, coherent beds of rock, that vary from less than 0.3 m to several metres in thickness with well developed vertical joints.

The sandstone beds are made up of many individual cemented layers of sand inclined at an angle to the bedding planes, a feature that is known as cross-bedding. It is created by currents during deposition of the sand and in undisturbed sites the cross-bedding dips in a south-southeasterly direction which indicates deposition by currents from the north-northwest. Predominantly yellow-grey in colour, the sands contain small quantities of an iron-rich mineral called glauconite which is green on fresh exposure and gives the rock formation its name, but it quickly weathers to a yellow-brown, rust-coloured mineral called limonite, and some layers are strongly stained and streaked brown or orange by this and other iron minerals.

Chert is chemically similar to the better-known flint found in the Chalk, and is formed largely, possibly entirely, by re-deposition of silica from the skeletal parts of sponges, known as spicules, that were originally intermixed in the sands. Light brown in colour, it is a hard, micro-crystalline material that occurs most commonly as thin, discontinuous lens-shaped masses but also as dispersed nodules. The chert reinforces the softer sands and sandstones that make up the majority of the Hythe Formation and makes them very resistant to erosion. In consequence they produce a bold escarpment overlooking the Vale of Fernhurst with an impressively steep scarp slope that descends 100 m or so to the flat, low ground of the vale below, which is underlain predominently by the Weald Clay.

At the top of the scarp slope, many of the joints in the sandstone layers are opened up and gape. These opened joints, known as 'gulls', are sometimes infilled with debris from above and result from joint-bounded blocks of sandstone moving apart due to bending and 'cambering' of the sandstone beds down the scarp slope. As a result of this process, the dip of the beds visible in some exposures can be very misleading because some sections are tilted down-scarp, whilst others have rotated on their base and lie back-tilted into the scarp. This can be seen in a number of locations where outcrops of individual beds of sandstone can be traced across the scarp, such as along the sides of the minor road from Easebourne to Lickfold as it crosses the scarp in the vicinity of Bexley Hill, and along the road and track that descends northwards from Woolbeding Common between Telegraph Hill and Older Hill.

Historically some of the harder sandstone and chert layers in the Hythe Formation were used for building stone and weaker bands for sand production. In consequence they are exposed in a number of former

The chert-reinforced sandstones of the Hythe Formation form an impressive escarpment overlooking the Vale of Fernhurst underlain mostly by soft clays of the Wealden Group.

ally fine grained sequence of rocks known as the Sandgate Formation. In places the lower part of this rock sequence comprise clays and loamy sands within which there are layers and lenses of a hard calcareous sandstone known as the Bargate Stone. Within the Park this stone is found around Midhurst where the Sandgate Formation reaches its maximum thickness of around 45 m. Elsewhere the deposits are dominated by loamy, iron-rich silts, clays and fine sands, often reddish-brown in colour, although around Selham a coarse sand characterized by smooth polished grains of limonite and known as the Selham Iron-shot Sands occurs. Around Pulborough the upper layers include a soft yellow-red sandstone known as the Pulborough Sandrock overlain by a dark-grey shaley clay known as the Marehill Clay.

quarries, most notably at Combe Hill on the road between Rogate and Rake, and at Little Bognor, north of Fittleworth. Some of the beds exposed at Combe Hill show interesting fold features that must have occurred during deposition, possibly due to slumping on the sea-floor. The Hythe Formation can also be inspected in numerous roadside and footpath exposures around Harting Coombe, Older Hill, Henley and

Bexley Hill on the south side of the Vale of Fernhurst and around Rake, Hollycombe and Blackdown to the north.

Deposition of the Hythe Formation ceased as a consequence of earth movements that caused gentle folding, faulting and uplift that was most severe to the north, before renewed inundation by the sea gave rise to deposition of a rather variable, but gener-

Despite their thickness, exposures of the Sandgate Formation are limited and occur primarily in sunken lanes, especially along minor roads crossing the Rother valley around South Ambersham, Selham and Shopham. The Pulborough Sandrock and Marehill Clay can be seen in old quarry and tunnel workings just outside the Park boundary immediately north of the A283 near Marehill, which is a Site of Special

The Sandgate Formation is most frequently comprised of soft silty clays that are exposed in a number of cuttings where minor roads ascend from the River Rother such as here near South Ambersham.

Pulborough Sandrock overlain by Marehill Clay exposed in old quarry workings near Pulborough.

Scientific Interest (SSSI). The site is not freely open to the public but can be visited under supervision of a warden at certain times of the year. Locally some Bargate Stone was used as a building stone, although not as commonly as further north in Surrey where outcrops were extensively worked around Godalming, but good examples of its use can be found around Woolbeding and just outside the park at Kirdford, including the church.

Above the Sandgate Formation lies the coarser Folkestone Formation. Predominantly these comprise poorly consolidated sands with occasional seams of pebbles or clay. The sands are mostly yellow to reddish-brown, but in some localities are almost uniformly dull red. Locally, hard brown to purple veins and masses of sand are cemented with iron compounds to

Quarry face exposing Folkestone Formation sands at Chantry Lane on the edge of Storrington, viewed from the foot of the Downs. This is one of a whole series of pits and quarries, most no longer actively worked, that lie along the outcrop of the Folkestone Formation.

form a tough rock sometimes referred to as 'carstone', or 'clinker'. A similar, but more persistent, iron-cemented layer of gritty sandstone lies at the junction with the overlying Gault. The sands display well-developed cross-bedding the direction of which indicates that the sediment was continuing to come from the northwest. It is thought that the sands represent large sand waves, possibly involving the reworking of submerged sand dunes, moving under strong, shallow-water currents. In common with the other members of the Lower Greensand, the Folkestone Formation thins from over 60 m in the west to around 30 m east of Pulborough, where it passes out of the Park. In East Sussex, part of the thinning outcrop is again included within the Park between Ditchling and Streat where the formation is around 15 m thick.

The outcrop of the Folkestone Formation can be traced very easily from west to east across the countryside because it gives rise to a series of 'commons' characterized by acidic heathlands and coniferous woodlands notably at West Heath, Trotton, Iping, Stedham, Midhurst, Heyshott, Ambersham, Graffham, Lavington, Duncton, Sutton, Hesworth, Fittleworth, Greatham, Rackham, Wiggonholt and Washington. The

© Ben du Boulay

Cemented sands in the Folkestone Formation at Rackham. The sands exhibit cross-bedding. Note also the characteristic wooded heathland vegetation that grows on these sterile sands.

Folkestone Formation has also been widely exploited for building sand and there are a number of large sand winning quarries and pits all along the outcrop. Most have ceased working but remain as industrial sites, often with building-related activities, whilst others have been used for landfill. In consequence, although there are large pits within the Park at West Heath, Minstead, Midhurst, Pendean and Duncton there is no

Hard iron-cemented sands and clays were used as building stones, either alone or mixed with other stones. Many examples can be found from Pulborough westwards along the north side of the Rother valley to Midhurst.

public access and the outcrops can only be visited by permission or viewed from afar. The bright yellow-red faces of the excavations can in particular be seen from the top of the Downs from where they are a very visible landscape feature — and not only those within the Park but also large pits at Storrington, Sullington and Washington, which lie immediately north of the Park boundary. There are also a large number of smaller pits in and around the commons such as at the crossroads on the southern edge of Ambersham Common, and by the car park at Rackham where the sands are sufficiently cemented to form low cliffs. Public footpaths running close to some of the working pits provide clear views of the sands.

The dark red-brown, sometimes purple, bands of hard ironstone were quarried at Fittleworth, Pulborough and Trotton and can be inspected in buildings, for it was used as a domestic building stone, especially around Pulborough and westwards along the Lower Greensand outcrop. Sometimes it was used in small quantities with other sandstones or clay ironstone, elsewhere as the sole or principal stone. Houses, usually stone-built, can be found also with small pieces of ironstone embedded in the mortar, a process known as 'galetting'. This was done either for a decorative effect or sometimes to help reinforce and strengthen the mortar of stone-built houses, especially those built of irregular rubble or freestone. There are good examples in Amberley, Easebourne, Pulborough, Sutton and many other West Sussex villages.

The Gault and Upper Greensand Formations

Finally, the shallow, coastal sea in which predominantly sandy deposits were laid down by strong currents, deepened and extended northwards and westwards to be replaced by calm, still-water conditions. In places, particularly in the west, this transition is marked by a thin layer of deepish red, iron-rich sandstone known as 'Iron Grit', but as the sea deepened from the east, fine mud was slowly deposited which produced a stiff, predominantly dark, bluish-grey clay known as the Gault. This is a very fossiliferous deposit, containing many bivalves, snails and, most notably, ammonites which underwent rapid evolution and change during this period. When wet the clay is very sticky and glutinous, but in dry summer weather it turns hard, shrinks and develops extensive interconnecting cracks.

Above the Gault lies the Upper Greensand which indicates the return of stronger currents bringing slightly coarser sediments into the sea. However, despite its name, within the area of Park the Upper Greensand is mostly neither green nor sandy. From where it outcrops in the west, close to the Hampshire border, east to Lewes, it comprises a pale white or dull grey calcareous siltstone known as malmstone. Only in the extreme east of the Park, around Eastbourne, is the rock green and sandy. Malmstone is mostly rather soft and friable with variable cementation. Nevertheless, some beds are sufficiently coherent for it to have been widely quarried in various localities for use as a building stone, especially from Pulborough westwards into East Hampshire. Many examples can be seen in and around Selborne — notably Plestor House, in Newton Valence, Blackmoor, Chawton, Hawley, Chidham, South Harting, Buriton, Elsted and Sutton, and less commonly further eastwards in villages such as Fulking.

The Upper Greensand deposits are thickest in the west of the Park, for whilst coarser grained deposits were being laid down

© David Robinson

Across most of the Park, the Upper Greensand is comprised of a soft silt-rich limestone known as malmstone which was widely used for buildings such as this example in the village of Sutton. Note the decorative galleting of the mortar with fragments of ironstone, and surface decay of the stone which is considerably less resistant to weathering than local sandstones.

here in the west, in quieter water conditions to the east, clays continued to be deposited. Thus, the Upper Greensand thins eastwards and grades into the Gault,

Gault clay overlying Folkstone Formation sands in the south face of the quarry at Chantry Lane. The sands were deposited in shallow water with strong currents, whilst the clay marks the arrival of deeper calmer water conditions.

the upper part of which is of the same age as some of the Upper Greensand deposits in the west. Both the Gault and the Upper Greensand are thickest in the west where the Gault approaches 100 m and the Upper Greensand over 60 m in thickness but the latter thins eastwards to less than 10 m at the eastern end of the Park, and appears to be totally absent in places between the Ouse valley and Eastbourne. In West Sussex, where the malmstone is best developed from Cocking through Petersfield and round to Selborne and beyond, the Upper Greensand forms a distinct low cuesta or bench at the base of the main Chalk escarpment, overlooking the Gault clay vale.

Lying at the foot of the steep Chalk scarp, much of the outcrop of both the Gault and the Upper Greensand is obscured by downwash of Chalk and flinty debris and nowhere is the Gault well exposed in natural vertical section. Historically it was dug from large pits near Rodmell in the Ouse valley, and just to the north of the Park at Small Dole in the Adur valley, to add to Chalk for cement manufacture at the Beddingham and Shoreham works respectively. It was dug also on a smaller scale for use in brick manufacture at places such as Ringmer, also just outside the Park boundary and is still dug for this

© David Robinson

Upper Greensand malmstone is exposed in numerous road-side exposures, especially in West Sussex including this site almost opposite the Shepherd and Dog public house in Fulking.

purpose within the Park at Pitsham, south of Midhurst, but there is no public access. The junction of the Lower Gault sitting above the sandy Folkestone Formation can be viewed in the southern face of a large sandpit south of Storrington just off the lane to Chantry Hill, but again there is no public access without prior permission of the owners.

In East Hampshire and West Sussex, the Upper Greensand is exposed in a number of road cuttings at the foot of the Downs escarpment, especially around Selborne. Another famous exposure is in the road cutting opposite the popular 'Shepherd and Dog' public house at Fulking, north of Brighton. Here, as in most other exposures

One of the rare exposures of malmstone not alongside a road can be inspected below the walls of Amberley Castle, adjacent to a public footpath.

the rock is a pale whitish-grey, blocky malmstone that at first sight looks very like impure Chalk. A similar exposure can be inspected on the narrow road that rises to Chantry Hill south from Storrington. One of the few good, easily accessible exposures not in a road cutting is in the footings of Amberley Castle adjacent to the public footpath that descends north of the castle, from the west end of the village.

In East Sussex, the Upper Greensand is particularly well exposed and can be safely inspected at the foot of the cliffs and on the foreshore west of Eastbourne in the vicinity of Cow Gap, where there is access to the shore, and from here westwards towards Beachy Head. Gault clay also outcrops on the foreshore at this locality, but not in the cliffs. However the geology is complex because it has been affected by massive ancient landslips that are now truncated, and cut across by the sea. In consequence, if you walk seawards from the foot of the access steps at Cow Gap, you cross from Grey Chalk, to the Upper Greensand to the Gault and then, if the tide is sufficiently low, you can cross several repeat sequences of these same rocks. The Greensand forms low ridges running along the shore which stand several metres above intervening, lower-lying areas underlain by Gault, that are often partially or wholly covered by thin beach shingle and a variety of larger cobbles. Further upstanding ridges of the Greensand lie seaward of the normal low-tide level enclosing sheltered, shallow-water lagoons that occupy further low-lying areas underlain by Gault. These can be seen impressively from the cliff-top access path leading to Cow Gap from the Holywell Café at the western end of King Edward's Parade, Eastbourne. Westwards from Cow Gap, the Upper Greensand forms a well-developed stepped platform that juts out

Ridges of Upper Greensand sandstone protect shallow lagoons underlain by Gault clay below the cliffs at Holywell, Eastbourne. The ridges result from differential erosion of the soft clay and are repeated because the sea has eroded across a series of ancient landslips each affecting both the Gault and the Greensand.

The Head Ledge, which projects out to sea at the foot of the cliffs just east of Beachy Head is composed of a hard, resistant sandstone that comprises the Upper Greensand Formation in the extreme east of the Park. The softer, less resistant Chalk, that once overlaid the sandstone has been eroded away and receded many tens of metres from the more seaward parts of the ledge to the present cliff line.

to sea, known as the Head Ledge. The beds here are undisturbed by landslipping and dip northwestwards towards the cliffs where they are overlain first by a sandy beach known as Falling Sands and then in the cliffs by the Grey Chalk.

The Upper Greensand that outcrops in this eastern extremity of the Park is very different from that seen further west. The lowest 2 m or so of the outcrop comprise a dark green, glauconitic sandstone. Above lies about 3 m of paler, more buff-coloured sandstone, that includes a prominent hard calcareous sandstone layer about 0.3 m thick. The remaining upper 2 m or so reverts to a dark green glauconitic sandstone distinguished by a thin hard, almost black band 2–10 cm thick at its base. Above, the sandstone grades into a light green-grey marl known as the Glauconitic Marl which forms the lowest bed of the Chalk. This difference in the character of the rocks and the fact that boreholes indicate that the Upper Greensand is entirely absent in places between Lewes and Eastbourne suggest that a shallow ridge separated two basins of deposition when the sediments were being laid down. The sandstone was quarried for use as a building stone in and around Eastbourne where it can still be seen today.

The varying layers of Upper Greensand can be inspected on the foreshore at Cow Gap where there is safe access down the cliffs. This photograph shows the upper layers overlain by the more eroded Glauconite Marl, from which small phosphatic nodules can be seen protruding, which forms the base of the Chalk. This is overlain by beds of more typical soft, Grey Chalk in the base of the cliffs above.

© Peter Anderton (RIGS/SBRC)

The Chalk

The Chalk that overlies the Upper Greensand, and forms the distinctive rounded uplands after which the Park is named, is a soft white limestone. It is comprised mostly of the calcareous remains of minute marine planktonic algae known as coccoliths that accumulated on the bottom of a sea of normal salinity over a period of 30–35 million years from approximately 100 to 65 million years ago. Initially clay, fine sand and silt were also deposited on the floor of the sea, probably brought in by rivers from a nearby land mass, but over time the sea became more extensive and much clearer, containing almost no non-biogenic material to settle on the floor. The sediment that formed the Chalk accumulated very slowly as an ooze on the floor of this sea at an overall average rate of about 0.5 mm a year. Over time, flexuring of parts of the sea floor occurred to produce an undulating surface. As a consequence, sedimentation on high points of the floor periodically ceased, probably because any sediment was washed off by underwater currents, and some of these high points actually underwent erosion. Debris from these areas accumulated in the downwarps in the sea floor. Areas where sedimentation ceased for periods

3 µm

A scanning electron micrograph of Chalk showing entire and broken rings of the minute skeletons of coccoliths of which it is largely composed. Scale bar, 3 µm = 0.003 of a millimeter.

tended to harden and form so-called 'hardgrounds' of denser, harder Chalk. The Chalk Sea appears to have deepened over time from a minimum 125 m to over 600 m during deposition of the upper White Chalk and at its maximum extent covered most of western Europe. Over the 30 million years or more of sedimentation several hundred metres of Chalk were deposited before earth movements occurred that raised the entire area above sea-level and ushered in a phase of sub-aerial erosion. An unknown amount of Chalk was eroded and the total thickness and exact date when sedimentation ceased in southeast England is therefore uncertain.

The coccoliths of which the Chalk is primarily composed can be seen only under high magnification such as electron microscopes, but fossil remains of larger organisms that lived in the Chalk Sea can be found. These macro-fossils include abundant echinoids (sea urchins), bivalves, coiled ammonites – some of which are a metre or more in diameter, and species of fish. Fossil echinoids and small ammonites can sometimes be found in the beach gravels at the foot of the cliffs. The coils of massive ammonites can sometimes be seen embedded in the surface of the shore platforms that stretch seawards

Examples of fossil echinoids (sea urchins) from the Chalk that can be found on many Sussex beaches below eroding cliffs.

from the cliffs. The occurrence of fossils is variable, with some beds and sections of the Chalk having large numbers, others very few.

This variation in fossil content is a characteristic feature of the Chalk, which at first sight looks remarkably homogeneous, but in reality is quite variable. Not only is there a variation in the distribution and abundance of macro fossils, but also in the ratio between calcium carbonate, clay and flint. The higher content of clay impurities in the lower parts of the Chalk formation makes the rock softer and less porous, and rather grey in colour. Formerly referred to as the Lower Chalk, these clay-rich lower beds are now known as the Grey Chalk. The younger overlying purer beds of Chalk are much whiter. Formerly known as the Middle and Upper Chalk, all these beds are now included within what is called the White Chalk, the upper parts of which frequently contain regularly spaced bands of dark-coloured flint.

Flint is a form of silica derived largely from the remains of masses of microscopic plankton such as diatoms and radiolaria, and a few larger organisms such as sponges that lived in the Chalk Sea but had skeletons composed of silica rather than calcium. On death their skeletal remains fell to the sea

A large ammonite exposed in the foreshore near Roedean. Large ammonites such as these lived in the Chalk Sea and fossil examples are periodically exposed along the coast by erosion of the Chalk shore platforms. Sadly this example has now been completely eroded away.

© Martin Eade

Flint is derived mostly from animals with silica skeletons that lived in the Chalk Sea. The silica dissolved and was re-precipitated during the transformation of the ooze that accumulated on the floor of the sea into the rock we call Chalk, often as layers, but also as more scattered nodules as can be seen in this block on the foreshore near Seaford Head.

© Peter Anderton (RIGS/SBRC)

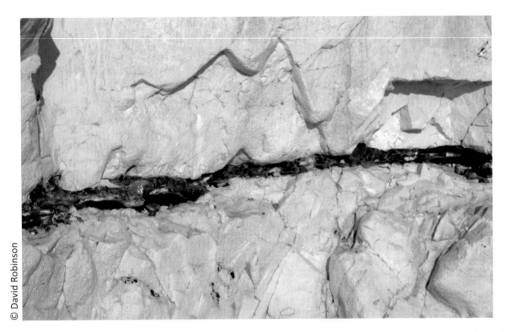

Horizontal sheets of flint often follow bedding planes *(left)*, or penetrate vertical joints *(right)*.

bed where they were incorporated into the predominantly calcareous sediment accumulating on the sea floor. As they became buried the skeletons dissolved and released their silica into the pore water circulating within the sediments. As the sediment gradually compacted, this dissolved silica was preferentially re-precipitated in certain locations, apparently determined largely by variations in the porosity and sulphur content of the sediment, which seem to have been associated with the localized accumulation of decaying organic matter. Flints within the Chalk occur mostly in one of two quite distinct forms. Layers of irregularly shaped nodular flints appear to have originated mostly as the infill of tunnels created by species that scavenged and burrowed in the accumulating sediments on the floor of the Chalk Sea. Thinner, flatter sheets of flint occur as layers along horizontal bedding planes within the Chalk. Similar thin sheets of flint also penetrate vertical or sub-vertical joints and fractures within the Chalk. Some flint seems to have formed very early during the compaction and lithification processes that converted the calcareous sediments into Chalk rock, but the existence of some flint as sheets along bedding planes, joints and fractures suggests that re-distribution and re-precipitation of silica must have continued for some considerable time after the initial hardening and lithification of the Chalk commenced. Flint is also found infilling and enveloping the shells of dead organisms such as echinoids, and in some localities such as at Seaford Head and Beachy Head, very large, columnar flints, known as 'Paramoudra' can be seen.

Variation in the character of the Chalk can best be inspected in the magnificent cliffs that stretch between Eastbourne and Brighton. The lower parts of the Chalk succession are particularly well exposed in the tall cliffs to the east of Beachy Head, in the vicinity of Head Ledge and Falling Sands, where they can be safely accessed via the steps at Cow Gap. Walking southwest along the top of the beach, the lowest bed, exposed at the foot of the cliff and the upper foreshore is a clay-rich, gritty calcareous sandstone known as the Glauconite Marl. The base of the marl is characterized by traces of intense burrowing that occurred at the time of its formation. Most widespread are the horizontal, cylindrical burrows of a prawn-like creature known as *Thalassinoides*, which are 2–3 cm in diameter with characteristic Y-shaped junctions that often join to form polygonal patterns. The fossils have been phosphatized which makes them more resistant to erosion than the rest of the marl, and there

Chalk Marl, Cow Gap. The lower parts of the Chalk Formation contain significant quantities of clay and silt which gives it the predominantly grey colour by which it is now named. Variation in the quantity of clay and silt present in different layers result in differences in colour and hardness. Grey clay-rich layers erode more easily than the harder, whiter layers containing less clay.

© Peter Anderton (RIGS/SBRC)

are also small brown, irregularly shaped phosphatic nodules that resist weathering and protrude from the surface of the marl matrix.

Above the Glauconite Marl lies the Chalk Marl which consists of thin beds of pale grey Chalk, averaging about 0.3 m in thickness, alternating with thicker beds of darker clay-rich marl. These pass upwards into a massive greyish-white Chalk, with thin marl seams, which forms the majority of the Grey Chalk. There is then a very distinctive series of dark grey-green clay-rich marl bands, each 2–3 m thick, known as the Plenus Marls, which form the base of the overlying White Chalk. The Plenus Marls can be seen descending southwestwards towards the shoreline which they meet at TQ5865 9540. Above this lies a very distinctive hard, yellow-white, nodular band of Chalk known traditionally as the Melbourn Rock. This is in turn overlain by further bands of white Chalk of varying hardness before we reach the first of a whole series of regularly spaced flint bands. The rocks are all dipping down to the southwest and as one walks westwards from Cow Gap the entire succession can be inspected at the base of the cliffs, although the flint-bearing Chalk reaches sea-level only some distance beyond the Lighthouse and great care needs to be taken with the tides to avoid being cut off. These flinty upper layers of Chalk can be more safely inspected elsewhere along the cliffs from access points at Birling Gap, Cuckmere Haven, Hope Gap and from the undercliff walkway between Brighton and Peacehaven. The cliff between Cow Gap and Beachy Head is, however, the best place to inspect the junction between the Upper Greensand and the Chalk, and to inspect the lower beds of the Grey Chalk. These are quite fossiliferous and a variety of ammonites, echinoids and brachiopods

can be found *in situ* within the cliffs and on the foreshore. Eastwards from Cow Gap, towards Eastbourne, the geology is complicated by faults and massive ancient landslides which results in Chalk beds of different ages outcropping in a complex and irregular sequence at sea-level including good sections of the Plenus Marls and the Melbourn Rock at what is known as the Pinnacle.

Within the Grey Chalk, it is sometimes possible to see dark-coloured, circular nodules a few centimetres in diameter, either embedded within the Chalk or sometimes protruding a little from the cliff face. Partly covered in a chalky patina, the freshly exposed surface of a nodule is dark grey or black, but on exposure it rapidly turns yellowish-ochre or rusts, sometimes creating rusty streaks on the white cliff face below. These are nodules of an iron mineral called marcasite which is a form of iron sulphide. The nodules are released from the cliffs by erosion of the surrounding Chalk and can sometimes be found lying on the beach or foreshore, often in a disintegrating state. Although dull and often rusty on the outside, internally they consist of shiny, metallic, gold-coloured radiating crystals. If collected, entire nodules remain sound,

Marcasite nodules from the Chalk. Examples can be seen in the cliffs and can sometimes be found on the foreshore at Cow Gap and other locations. Inside they are comprised of silvery-gold radiating crystals of iron sulphide.

but if cracked or broken open the metallic sheen soon develops a soft powdery surface due to reaction with oxygen in the air and the nodules begin to disintegrate.

The White Chalk is divided into a series of distinct beds, which differ somewhat in character. Beds in the lower part of the formation are flint-free whilst the upper beds have more regular bands of flint and in general the proportion of flint increases upwards. Some beds are fossilferous whilst others are almost free of fossils. Beds vary also in hardness, in thickness, in jointing patterns and in their degree of fissuring. For long stretches the beds exposed in the cliffs are horizontal or dip very gently, especially along the Seven Sisters Coast between Birling Gap and Cuckmere Haven. West of the Cuckmere, the dip of the beds becomes more variable because of flexuring and faulting of the Chalk, especially around Seaford Head. Minor faulting can be observed through displacement, often by less than 1 m, of horizontal flint bands on either side of the faults.

The cliffs are eroding quite rapidly, and if the foot of the cliffs is approached, care needs to be taken for small pieces of rock frequently fall off the cliffs and the wearing of a hard hat is always to be recommended. The cliff foot should never be approached in cold frosty weather when freeze–thaw action can release large quantities of debris, especially during thawing. Larger cliff falls occur mostly during stormy conditions when both the cliff edge and cliff foot should be avoided.

Rhythmically spaced flint bands are a characteristic feature of much of the White Chalk and are well displayed in cliff sections such as here, west of Birling Gap.

© David Robinson

Grassed-over Chalkpits on the Downs at Saddlescombe. Scars of such former working of the Chalk are widespread on many steep slopes.

Over the years Chalk has been excavated and used for a variety of agricultural and industrial purposes which has left many scars on the physical landscape, but in consequence there are numerous inland locations where the Chalk can be inspected. For geologists some of these, especially in the Ouse and Arun valleys such as the Southerham Grey Pit south of Lewes are of national or international importance, and several require prior permission before entry. However, for the casual amateur, none are as good or as easy to access as the sea cliffs, nor are they as good for gaining an overall impression of the variation existing within the Chalk and of its minor structures, because each quarry face usually exposes only a small section of the thick Chalk sequence.

The oldest use of the Chalk was probably simply as crushed and broken rock to improve the 'heavy and sour' soils of the Weald. Chalk helps to improve the 'workability' and lower the acidity of such soils. The Chalk was mostly extracted from small pits dug into the steep north-facing scarp slope of the Downs. Some of these were single pits of varying sizes, others such as those on Malling Down, Lewes and above settlements such as Keymer, Steyning,

© Ben du Boulay

An old Chalk quarry immediately adjacent to the River Arun. Prior to rail and road development, water was important for the transport of Chalk and lime, both inland into the Weald and to the coast.

Storrington and many other villages were extensive complexes used repeatedly over very long periods of time. It was later discovered that heating the Chalk to produce lime reduced the Chalk to a powdery clin-

ker and greatly increased its solubility. This resulted in much larger-scale production and with improvements in transport, initially canalization of the rivers, then later the arrival of railways and modern roads,

Pyecombe Chalk Quarry, one of the few remaining Chalk quarries in the Park.

much larger quarries developed, especially in the major valleys through which the rivers, railways and roads were routed, such as around Lewes, Shoreham, Lower Beeding (Goldring Farm) and Amberley, and also in wind gaps, such as at Cocking and Duncton, through which transport links also ran. Another major use of lime was for mixing with sand to produce a building mortar. At the time of writing only two of these quarries are still actively worked — in the 'wind gaps' at Pyecombe and Duncton — but the scars of other quarries can still be seen, many in various stages of recolonization by vegetation. The remnants of small limekilns in which the Chalk was burnt can also be found in and around the Downs such as in the Findon Gap, south of Washington and on the scarp slope near Fulking. Larger ones can be seen at the museum housed in the quarry at Amberley, and adjacent to the old quarry at Cocking. Chalk was often transported to be burnt in kilns north of the Downs and a good example survives at Ebernoe. On a smaller scale, Chalk and lime was used for a variety of other purposes, including; lime-wash which was used not just for decoration, but to help strengthen and waterproof many building surfaces, and in the mid 20th century, the production of 'Artex' wall and ceiling coatings from

quarries in the Ouse valley at Newhaven and Tarring Neville.

Chalk from the Downs was also used extensively for the production of Portland Cement. This requires a mixture of Chalk and clay which is burnt together at a temperature of around 1500°C. About 6% Gypsum is then added to the powdered clinker as a setting agent. Some beds of impure Grey Chalk contain sufficient clay that no more needs to be added, but most Chalk required the addition of clay that was imported from pits dug in the Gault or Weald clays to north of the Downs. As with the later limeworks, most cement works were located adjacent to the transport routes passing through the river valleys, with major works in the Ouse valley at Southerham and Beddingham, and in the Adur valley north of Shoreham. All have now ceased to work, Beddingham has been almost entirely infilled and is in the process of being re-landscaped and grassed over, Southerham has been converted into industrial premises, but the works north of Shoreham remain a prominent and problematic eyesore.

Any flint within the Chalk had to be removed before burning and this was a valuable by-product which was exported to

Entrance to an overgrown lime kiln near Washington. Remains of the quarry that supplied the kilns lies on the slopes immediately above.

the 'Potteries' for use in the glazing of fine china. Fresh grey flints were also collected from many of the beaches and exported north for the same purpose. Flint was also used extensively for building. Local flints from the Downs were irregular in shape and usually had to be knapped in various ways before they could be used satisfactorily for building purposes. In consequence,

Flint was widely used as a building material in various forms, but was nearly always combined with brick or stone to create corners, windows and door openings: *(top left)* round flint beach cobbles with brick; *(top right)* irregular downland flints with an embedded piece of iron-rich sandstone; *(bottom left)* knapped flints with sandstone; *(bottom right)* irregular downland flints galetted with flint chips and flakes.

Remnants of old flint workings at Cissbury hillfort. Shafts were dug into the Chalk until a good layer of flint was found, when radiating galleries were then dug to extract the flint.

© John Manley

Chalk used for interior stonework in North Stoke church. Relatively hard layers of Chalk such as the Melbourn Rock, which were easy to carve, were used quite extensively for interior work where they could not be attacked by the weather.

mines that comprised vertical shafts dug in Chalk hilltops leading to extensive galleries several metres below the ground, that followed favoured seams of flint. The remnants of these pits can still be seen in the form of hollows and hummocks on many hilltops throughout the Downs. The summits of hills lying on either side of the Findon Gap including Cissbury, Church Hill, Blackpatch and Harrow Hill appear to have been particularly important and have major concentrations of old workings, while others further west include Long Down, Stoke Down and Nore Down.

Most Chalk was too weak and porous to provide stone for domestic building, but some of the denser beds such as the Melbourn Rock are sufficiently strong to be used as building stone. It was, for example, used in churches, mostly for interior work, where it could be easily carved and was protected from the weather. An important source was the Chalk pit at Amberley and extensive use of the stone can be seen nearby in the interior of the church at North Stoke. It was used also in some cottages and farm buildings, although often only to a limited extent and mostly in areas protected from the weather, because all Chalk is porous and when damp is susceptible to frost damage.

many flints were imported into the Downs from the coast, as can be seen from their smooth, rounded appearance. Flints were unsuited for creating corners of buildings or sharp-angled edges for doors and windows and thus had to be combined with other materials, usually brick, imported from works exploiting clays either lying north of

the Downs, or overlying them to the south. Flint was used also for galleting, often stacked on edge in considerable quantities within the mortar rather than face on.

During Neolithic times, flints were mined from the Chalk for making a variety of tools. Many of these were obtained from

Hard Chalk used as exterior building stone in a converted barn in Amberley. Chalk was rarely used for exterior masonry except in farm buildings because of its high porosity and susceptibility to deterioration when exposed to the weather. When used it was often protected by over-hanging eaves.

Lavant, and possibly elsewhere, in quarries that have all now disappeared, the stone was used from Roman times until at least the 14th century. It was used in the building of important medieval buildings such as parts of Chichester Cathedral and Boxgrove Priory as well as in numerous other churches within the Park in West Sussex and East Hampshire.

Uplift and emergence of the land from the sea

Deposition of the Chalk was brought to an end by major earth movements that raised the whole of southeast England above sea-level. The emerging land was squeezed from the south by plate movements which domed the rocks along a line through central Sussex, across what is now the English Channel, which did not then exist, and into the Boulonnais region of northern France; whilst to the north and south the rocks were squeezed down to form the London and Hampshire Basins respectively. Minor folding occurred also along the main limbs of the central dome and the folding was accompanied by faulting, where some of the stress was released by breakage of the rocks. All these minor folds and most of the faults are aligned in approximately the same west-northwest to east-southeast

Occasional use can be seen in places such as Elsted, Cocking and Harting in the West Sussex, and in villages in the Meon valley in Hampshire. Another Chalk used extensively in medieval times was a localized dense spicular bed of Chalk that weathers grey, and is known as Lavant Stone. Quarried in the Chilgrove valley near the village of

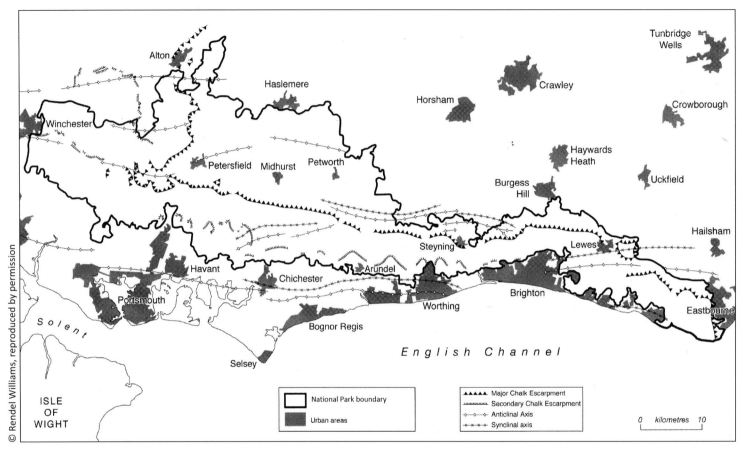

The geological structure of the National Park showing anticlines (lines of local uplift) and synclines (lines of local downwarping) resulting from the earth movements that created the Wealden dome. Note how the line of the Chalk scarp is influenced by these structures and the position of the line of hills known as the 'secondary scarp' capped by Culver Chalk (see pp. 53–4 for details).

direction as the main anticlinal dome, at approximate right angles to the direction of pressure. Uplift was slow and probably intermittent throughout much of the ensuing geological period known traditionally as the Tertiary, but which today comprises what are known as the Palaeogene and the Neogene. As the land emerged, rivers flowed north and south draining and eroding this domed land surface and began to erode the Chalk. Just how much Chalk was eroded is uncertain but it is believed to have been many tens, and in places probably hundreds of metres. The large south flowing rivers that today cut through the eastern Downs in magnificent river gaps possibly originated on this land surface.

Palaeogene inundation and deposition

After emerging from the Chalk Sea, southeast England remained a land mass, subject to sub-aerial erosion for 10 million years or more before much of it was re-submerged by a transgressive sea that gradually flooded the land and deposited a series of gravels, sands and clays. This transgression marks the arrival of the Palaeogene. Submersion was greatest around the margins of the emerging dome, in the down-warped London and Hampshire Basins where thick

Sands and clays of the Lambeth Group, overlying White Chalk with regularly spaced bands of flint at West Cliff, Newhaven.

deposits of sand and clay were laid down. This included the area that is now the Sussex Coastal Plain, which is an easterly extension of the Hampshire Basin. Just how much of southeast England was submerged at this time remains uncertain, but during the

maximum of the transgression most, probably all, of the Chalk of the South Downs was submerged and deposits of sands and clays laid down over the entire surface. These deposits still overlie the Chalk where it dips southwards under the coastal plain

Close-up of the Lambeth Group at West Cliff, Newhaven, showing the basal bed of cemented rolled flints lying on the eroded upper surface of the underlying Chalk.

very disturbed remnants can be seen sitting on top of the cliffs at Seaford Head and can sometimes be inspected on the beach after cliff falls.

However, they can be observed in detail at a site a little outside the Park, sitting on top of the Chalk at the West Cliff, Newhaven. Here, with care, they can be inspected at close quarters by ascending the cliff up shutes of sand and clay that descend to the beach down what are probably large solution hollows, where acidified water passing through the sands and clays has dissolved the underlying Chalk. Ascending one of these shutes, one can first observe closely the beds of the White Chalk with characteristically rhythmic bands of flint. The top surface of the Chalk is slightly uneven and is overlain by a layer of rolled and broken flint pebbles, mostly stained green or black. These pebbles show evidence of wave action and are of marine origin, deposited in a shallow, near-shore environment as the sea submerged the Chalk. The surface on which they rest is known as the sub-Palaeogene surface and there is an age gap of probably 20 million years possibly greater between the age of the pebble deposit and the top of the eroded Chalk on which they rest. As the pebbles are composed

of West Sussex and East Hampshire, but over most of the South Downs they have nearly all been removed by erosion, or been severely disturbed by frost churning during the later Quaternary Ice Ages. On the East Sussex Downs they are preserved only in a few synclinal (downwarped) areas such as around Falmer on the northeastern edge of Brighton. Nowhere within the Park are they exposed for inspection, although

of flint, they must have been derived from erosion of the Chalk, but not from that on which they directly sit as they have been rounded and eroded over a period of time by marine action as occurs on beaches at the present day. Overlying the pebble bed are approximately 10 m of variably coloured sands and sandy clays that contain many fossil leaves and shells and bands of black lignite, and lignitic clays some of which contain very good rectilinear crystals of a clear mineral called Selenite, a form of Gypsum. These deposits are finally capped by a bed of oyster shells overlain by clay. All these sands and clays form what are known as the Woolwich Beds that lie within the Lambeth Group. Overlying the oyster bed the deposits grade into heavier grey clays that are part of the London Clay, of which only the lowest 5 m or so survive. All are heavily disturbed by landslipping and by attempts to stabilize the deposits by drainage works. All these deposits were laid down over a period of 10 million years or so commencing approximately 60 million years ago, after when the sea retreated again.

The small patch of these deposits that survive around the village of Falmer, on the eastern fringe of Brighton include the basal bed of rolled flints, overlain by 3 to 4 m of

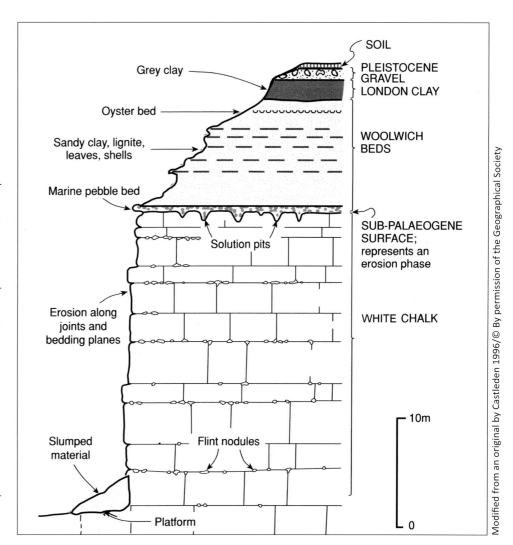

Rock layers visible at West Cliff, Newhaven.

Modified from an original by Castleden 1996/© By permission of the Geographical Society

© David Robinson

Reddened 'clay-with-flints' overlying Chalk, evidence that a covering of Palaeogene deposits was once widespread across the Downs.

form low hills, mostly covered in woodland, growing on rather heavy, poor draining soils. In places, the clay-rich deposits support small streams which, when they flow off the clays, disappear down small swallow holes into the underlying Chalk. Examples can be seen around the outliers at Clapham, Patching and westwards towards Warningcamp.

Elsewhere on the Downs thin surviving remnants of these Palaeogene deposits have lost all traces of bedding structure as a consequence of churning by frost action during the Quaternary cold periods, when they were enriched also with a wind-blown silt known as loess. In many places they comprise a mixture of flints embedded in reddened clay with variable amounts of sand, in a deposit known as 'clay-with-flints'. In winter the distribution of these deposits can be traced by the red-brown colour of the overturned soils which contrast with the greyish-black colour of soils developed directly over the Chalk. Reddening of soils occurs in climates warmer than currently occur in southern Britain and this is one piece of evidence that sometime in the relatively recent geological past, probably during an interglacial, the climate of Britain was warmer than at the present day.

sandy clays. The deposits are not visible for inspection, but historically the thicker, sandier soils developed on these deposits helped to support market gardening to supply Lewes and Brighton, and have caused instability problems for the carriageway and road cutting of the A27 as it bisects the village.

In West Sussex, the coastal plain lying south of the Park is underlain by Palaeogene deposits. Where the Chalk dips below these deposits the northern limit of their outcrop is marked by a subdued north-facing escarpment, especially from Arundel westwards. To the north, outliers of these Palaeogene deposits survive on the lower dip slopes of the Chalk where they

Sarsen stones in *(top left)* Stanmer Park, at *(top right)* Rock Pond, Standean, and *(bottom left)* around the old village pump, Falmer. Formerly scattered across the Downs, Sarsens are now concentrated in a few off-farm locations to where they have been re-located over the centuries.

Scattered across the surface of the Downs are blocks of hard siliceous sandstone known as Sarsens. Large numbers can be found around the village of Falmer, surrounding the old village pump and pond; in Stanmer Park surrounding the green and pond by the church and further north in Rocky Clump, and at Rock Pond, Standean, to the north of Brighton. Elsewhere most occur as occasional isolated blocks, often on the edge of roads or trackways. Most are light grey-brown in colour, between one-half and two cubic metres in size and sub-angular to sub-rounded in form, although

© David Robinson

© Peter Anderton (RIGS/SBRC)

Close-up of two contrasting Sarsen stones with *(left)* a smooth surface and *(right)* a surface pitted with small cup-shaped hollows.

occasionally they are more angular and tabular. Outer surfaces are often smooth but sometimes irregular, with variably sized hollows and small pits. They are comprised predominantly of sand grains cemented by secondary overgrowths of silica. Occasional blocks are larger and some are rougher and more angular, sometimes containing flints bonded within the finer sandstone matrix.

Sarsens are remnant blocks of silcrete that developed in the sandy Palaeogene deposits that overlay the Chalk. Silcretes are created by the precipitation of silica in surface or near-surface environments, but this can occur under a variety of conditions. Initially, Sarsens were considered to be remnants of a silcrete that developed widespread across the Downs, very slowly, 30–35 million years ago, as a hard, cemented layer within soils developed under a seasonal, tropical or sub-tropical climate. However, more recent studies suggest their internal structure better accords with more localized sil-

cretes that develop by the evaporation of silica-rich groundwater along drainage lines, under hot, but not necessarily seasonally humid conditions. This may explain their concentrated distribution in some downland localities and absence from others and, because such silcretes can develop more rapidly and under a range of climates, they may be of considerably younger age. Most are found on the eastern Downs where the former Palaeogene cover appears to have been more sandy than further west.

Whatever their origin, the silcrete layers were severely disrupted and blocks moved downslope and down-valley by freeze–thaw related slope processes during cold periods of the Quaternary, the last of which ended only around 10,000 years ago. In addition, there has been a long history of re-distribution of these stones to clear arable fields and for use as building material. Today, many are located around ponds, some are known to have been buried by farmers and some have been moved off the Downs entirely. For example, there are a considerable number of Sarsens around the village pond in Ditchling immediately to the north of the Downs. A number are incorporated also into the lower walls of many Downland churches and in the boundary walls of churchyards. Elsewhere on the chalklands of southern England, outside the Park, Sarsens were used in the construction of prehistoric monuments such as Avebury Stone Circle and parts of Stonehenge, but there are no such surviving monuments on the South Downs and no certainty that any ever existed.

It is possible that at least eastern parts of the Park were submerged for a final time towards the end of the Neogene. Scattered sands containing marine fossils of Pliocene age have been found near Beachy Head, but they are something of a mystery, and any inundation must have been very short-lived for it appears to have had no significant impact on the landscape.

Quaternary deposits

Towards the end of the Neogene, the climate began to cool, ushering in the most recent geological period, the Quaternary. Commencing approximately 2.6 million years ago, the Quaternary has been characterized by dramatic climate oscillations with periods of sometimes extreme cold, separated by intervening warmer periods, when the climate was often as warm, or sometimes warmer than at the present day. During some of the cold periods, in what are often referred to as 'Ice Ages', glacial ice covered much of the British landscape north of the Thames, but the Downs were never glaciated. They suffered what is known as a periglacial climate in which the extreme cold permanently froze the ground to great depth, a condition known as permafrost. The surface thawed to a shallow depth in summer and freeze–thaw processes were very active, especially in spring and autumn.

It was during these periods of extreme cold that the youngest geological material to be deposited widespread across the Park originated. This is a glacially derived, wind-blown silt known as loess. A product of the glacial abrasion of rocks by ice, loess was derived from fine-grained material deposited close to the front of glaciers by meltwater during the ice ages. This was many tens of miles to the north and east of the South Downs, but these fine deposits were blown south and deposited widely across the landscape south of the ice limits, not just in southeast England, but in a zone south of the ice across much of western Europe and beyond. Loess is thought to have been deposited over the whole of southeast England, but most has since been removed by erosion. It is particularly vulnerable to erosion when saturated and appears to have survived on parts of the Chalk Downs only because the underlying rock is very free-draining. Even on the Chalk, survival as a distinct surface depositional layer is very limited, for most has been lost through erosion or incorporated into the thin soils, most of which contain significant quantities of silt.

Pure loess is a biscuit-coloured, free-draining, fine-grained silt material, entirely free of stones, but partially bonded by calcite (calcium carbonate) which sometimes shows as scattered patches of a white floury

© David Robinson

Fine-grained loess-rich deposits lying above the Chalk at Short Cliff, between Hope Gap and Cuckmere Haven. The loess here sits on, and is intermixed with, a complex of gravels of uncertain origin that over lie the Chalk.

Under a British climate, the carbonate within the loess tends to be dissolved by rainwater percolating through the deposit. This results in the upper parts becoming decalcified and as a consequence it can become rather acidic. At Lullington Heath on the Chalk Downs to the east of the Cuckmere Valley patches of loess have become decalcified in this way allowing acid-loving plants such as heathers to colonize and grow. This has produced a very unusual vegetation community known as 'chalk heath' which is comprised of some plants that like acid soils and others that like chalk-rich soils, and it is a National Nature Reserve. Smaller patches of similar acidic soils can be found overlying the Chalk elsewhere on the Downs, including at Ditchling Beacon.

Acidification of the rainwater passing through these overlying deposits of loess, and remnants of Palaeogene deposits accentuates solution of the Chalk beneath. Consequently the deposits often occupy hollows, or have descended down solution pipes, a metre or more in diameter that descend several metres into the Chalk. Very good examples of solution pipes can be seen exposed in cross-section in coastal cliffs at a number of localities in East Sussex, most notably at Short Cliff east of Seaford Head

deposit within the silt. It is nowhere clearly exposed inland, except during temporary excavations, and the only sections are in inaccessible cliff-top locations along the coast. One of the best, and thickest of these is at Short Cliff between Hope Gap and Cuckmere Haven. Inspection of disturbed deposits can be made here on the beach after cliff falls, but because of the nature of the material it is very quickly washed away after a few tides. A particularly interesting feature that can sometimes be found are 'loess dolls' These comprise small nodular concretions of loess cemented more strongly than normal by calcium carbonate, some of which can look like small figurines.

and just outside the Park at Telscombe, immediately east of the Portabello sewage outfall. At Short Cliff, some pipes descend the full height of the cliffs and the truncated base of several pipes can be identified on the shore platform many metres seaward of the present cliffs. Comprising circular hollows a metre or more in diameter, several exhibit a raised circular rim of Chalk that has been hardened by re-precipitated calcium carbonate derived from within the pipe. At low tide the hollow within the rim traps seawater and the truncated pipes can look like the remnants of built circular constructions, rather than entirely natural features. The Chalk lying immediately below loess deposits can undergo a similar hardening process and large blocks of such hardened Chalk can be found in remnants of past cliff falls close to the cliffs.

At the end of the last ice age, the loess is thought to have probably been a metre or more deep, but from Neolithic times onwards, clearance of the native woodland that covered the Downs led to the onset of erosion and removal of most of the loess. The erosion carried most of the loess out of the Downs entirely, but transported, re-deposited remnants survive partially infilling the floors of many of the present

Solution pipes descending deep into the underlying Chalk, sectioned by cliff retreat at Short Cliff, east of Hope Gap.

day dry valleys, where it is often intermixed with stones of flint and Chalk in a deposit known as 'Coombe Rock'. In West Sussex and Hampshire, loess that has been eroded and reworked by water forms a deposit known as 'brickearth' which covers much of the coastal plain, including the marginal areas that lie within the Park. At the exits of Chalk dry valleys, large fans of flint-dominated Coombe Rock also overlie parts of the inner coastal plain, where they have been extensively quarried, especially in the vicinity of Chichester, primarily for use in the ready-mix concrete industry.

The circular base of a deep solution pipe lost to cliff retreat are preserved in the inter-tidal platform east of Hope Gap; the edges of the solution pipes are hardened with re-precipitated calcium carbonate and frequently form a raised wall surrounding the water-filled base.

Soils of the Chalk and overlying deposits

Soils developed directly over the Chalk are today typically no more than 0.3 m in depth, contain abundant fragments of Chalk and flint, and are highly calcareous. They contain also a significant quantity of silt-sized material which is the remnant of the former cover of loess that is incorporated into the soils. Under woodland or grassland the soils are rich in humus and dark brown or black, but when cultivated they lose humus and become paler. These soils are known as rendzinas and the thinness of the soils and a lack of soil moisture during dry summers restricts their agricultural value. Nevertheless, on all but the scarp and the steeper valley side slopes above about 15 degrees they are now extensively cultivated mostly for crops of cereals, rape and linseed (also known as flax).

In valley bottoms, the rendzinas thicken and grade into deeper, more moisture retentive and less calcareous soils which, although sometimes flinty, with micronutrient deficiencies that discourage the growth of some crops, give good yields of cereals. Similar soils are found along the foot of the Downs, developed on hillwash overlying the lower Chalk, Upper Greensand and parts of the Gault clay outcrop. These soils are less flinty, but often contain

A freshly ploughed, stony, grey-black Rendzina soil, typical of those that develop directly over the Chalk. When cultivated the soils lighten in colour over time to become pale or whitish-grey due to the loss of organic matter.

Chalk soil enriched with Palaeogene deposits. The surface soil is dark grey and free-draining, but at depth the soil is reddened and clay-rich, resulting in poor drainage.

substantial quantities of Chalk and are the most highly valued agricultural soils in the Park.

On those areas of the Chalk overlain by remnants of Palaeogene deposits, the soils tend to be browner in colour and much less free-draining as a result of the presence of clays. Whilst the upper part of the soils are often relatively free-draining with an open structure of well-aggregated soil crumbs, at depth, the proportion of clay increases due to the redeposition of clay particles washed down from the upper soil by drainage water. This clay layer is sufficient to impede drainage and result in waterlogging of the soils, especially in winter. In areas of 'clay-with-flints', the clay accumulation zone is usually reddish in colour. Reddening of soils occurs only under warmer climatic conditions than exist in southern Britain at the present day and this suggests that the clay was washed down and the reddening developed during a past climatic period that was warmer than today, most likely during a recent past inter-glacial. Because the soils tend to be moisture retentive, and very wet in winter, they are difficult to work and large areas are used for forestry.

The scenery
of the Chalk

The Chalk escarpment

The Chalk outcrop of the South Downs forms the southern and western rim of the Weal-den Anticline where it creates an impressive horseshoe-shaped area of upland with a steep inward-facing escarpment and gently sloping dip slope, dissected by dry valleys. Walking along the crest of the scarp, or viewing the Downs from the low land to the north, one of the most noticeable characteristics is the relative consistency of its summit height. There is a slight overall rise from east to west, but there is surprisingly little variation in the crest height either within or between each Chalk block.

The landscape is comprised predominantly of flat or gently rounded hill tops that curve down into steep valley side slopes that lead to relatively flat-floored valley bottoms lacking any streams. The underlying Chalk is everywhere soil covered except for the scars of quarry workings, most of which are no longer active and are gradually becoming covered in soil and vegetation. Beneath their soil cover, the surface layers of Chalk

© Ben du Boulay

Walkers descending the steep north-facing scarp of the Chalk Downs above Fulking.

are generally more fissured and broken than those below. This can be observed in cliff and quarry faces and is thought to be the result of frost action, most probably under periglacial conditions during the Quaternary. Where there are thin overlying deposits of sand or loess, these can

(Right) Dip-slope valleys within the chalk such as this example between Brighton and Lewes exhibit rounded slopes characteristic of water-eroded landscapes, but lack perennial streams along their floors.

Created under periglacial conditions, involutions comprise pockets of soil and other superficial material that descend in pockets into the Chalk beneath. Seen here in the cliff-top behind Brighton Marina, notice how pieces of fractured Chalk have moved upwards between the pockets and reach into the overlying fine material. The Chalk has been broken also by frost action for considerable depth below the involutions.

often be seen to descend downwards for 50 cm or more into the broken Chalk, in rhythmically spaced pockets called 'involutions'. These features were created by the periglacial freeze–thaw processes acting on geological materials with differing porosity and thermal characteristics. Between the pockets the thin frost-shattered layers of Chalk bend upwards and in some cases stand vertical. Involutions can be observed from a distance at the top of the cliffs, espe-

cially from the undercliff walkway east from Brighton Marina to Saltdean, and in the vicinity of Birling Gap. They can be inspected more closely near the top of the path that descends from the Roedean Café to the undercliff at the east end of the Marina, and at other access points that descend the cliffs between Brighton and Peacehaven.

The steep scarp slope, which rises often 200 m or more above the Gault clay vale

below, is undoubtedly the most dramatic feature of the Chalk landscape. It is not a smooth continuous slope, but is variously indented by scallop-shaped hollows and short valleys known as 'coombs'. In places, particularly in the east, it exhibits a stepped profile with a forward-protruding bench part-way down that is capped by the resistant Melbourn Rock protecting the softer Grey Chalk below. As the line of the scarp traverses the countryside, it periodically steps forward and back as a consequence of erosion acting on several small folds and faults, created during uplift of the Central Wealden anticline, that are aligned *en-echelon* close to the present position of the scarp (see map p. 38). Tracing the scarp from east to west, the scarp first steps forward by approximately 5 km at Glynde, some 4 km east of Lewes. This is the result of a complex flexure that comprises two asymmetric pitching anticlines, the Beddingham anticline and the Kingston anticline separated by the Glynde syncline with a further syncline, the Caburn syncline, lying a little further north. Erosion by the Ouse and the Glynde rivers has unroofed the anticlinal structures to expose the underlying Gault and excavated the large, oval lowland south of Lewes known as the of the Vale of Brooks. In contrast,

(Top right) Traced across the countryside the face of the Chalk scarp is not a regular slope, but is mostly indented by a variety of shallow scallop-shaped hollows such as here along the stretch west of Devil's Dyke.

(Bottom right) The Vale of Brooks, south of Lewes where the River Ouse and its tributary Glynde Reach have eroded through an anticlinal fold in the Chalk to produce in-facing Chalk scarps. Note also terracettes formed by down-slope movement of the soil on the slope in the foreground.

© David Robinson

© Ben du Boulay

© Airscapes.co.uk

Major step-backs in the position of the Chalk scarp, such as this one between Newtimber Hill on the left and Poynings, are a result of erosion acting on east–west aligned folds created during uplift of the land.

to the northeast, Mount Caburn, which overlooks the Brooks from a height of 150 m, is structurally a synclinal trough — the entire landscape forming a classic example of inverted relief, with the zone of anticlinal uplift now an area of low ground and the synclinal trough now an upland.

Further west, the scarp steps back by over 3 km between Wolstonbury Hill and the Devil's Dyke at Poynings. This is associated with a large synclinal fold lying north of the Park that runs through Warminghurst and Henfield, and an asymmetric anticline, steeper on its north side, that runs through

Ashington and Pyecombe. The scarp then displays a further step forward of more than 3 km west of the Arun in the vicinity of Sutton as a consequence of the denudation of the east–west trending Greenhurst anticline and associated Wiggonholt syncline. Continuing west, the scarp is considerably indented, but there are no further major steps. Beyond Petersfield the entire scarp swings north, because the westward-dipping Wealden dome has not yet been denuded of its Chalk cover.

West of Brighton, a line of prominent, asymmetric hills, with their steepest slope facing north, run east–west across the dip slope of the Downs. Rising 60–70 m above the descending dip slope to their north, the hills continue westwards into Hampshire and form a discontinuous secondary escarpment which includes the well-known landmark of Cissbury Hill, north of Worthing (see map p. 38). They are everywhere capped by a sequence of Chalk beds known as Culver Chalk which appears to be more resistant to erosion than the Chalk below which has suffered greater erosion. There remains uncertainty as to the properties of the different Chalk beds that may account for this difference in resistance to erosion, but suggestions include variations in purity, in porosity, in the frequency of reinforcing flint bands and in their joint and fracture patterns.

A distinctive micro-feature of the steep, uncultivated grass slopes of the Downs, especially the scarp slope, are terracettes. These comprise tiers of regularly spaced, narrow, terrace-like features that follow the contours of the slope with vertical or near vertical risers and level or near level top surfaces. Most are of the order of 20–30 cm in width and the same in height, but narrower and taller terracettes also occur, especially on very steep sections of slope. Developed usually on grassed slopes, the upper surface may be partially bare due to animals walking along them and the risers may also be bare, exposing the soil and sometimes the poorly con-solidated frost-damaged Chalk beneath. The exact mechanisms responsible for creating terracettes remain uncertain, but they are primarily a product of the downslope, gravitational movement of the rather loosely consolidated, thin, friable soils that overlie the Chalk, by a process referred to as soil creep. Sheep, cattle and other animals, including peo-ple, walking along the tops of the risers undoubtedly assist in their development and it is suggested that the expansion

© Airscapes.co.uk

Terracettes, resulting from soil moving downslope, are a common feature of steep, grassed slopes on the Downs such as here at the Long Man of Wilmington. The thin soils here have also been eroded to expose the underlying Chalk, and old, grassed-over pits can be seen on the gentler slopes above.

and contraction of soil particles on hill-sides, as they undergo wetting and drying cycles, may be important, as may the fibrous root structure of grasses.

Dry valleys and associated features

Away from the scarp, the most noticeable feature of the Downland landscape is the almost complete lack of surface-water flow under all except the most exceptional rainfall events. This lack of surface water is because rain falling on the Downs either soaks into the Chalk, which is highly porous, or passes through the rock down joints and fissures. Only on those rare occasions when intense rainstorms supply water at a rate greater than the Chalk and overlying soils can absorb it does water flow over the surface, and this usually only for very short time periods. However, despite the volume of water that enters the Chalk, the current water table mostly lies far below the valley floors, and the water emerges only from springs along the scarp foot.

Despite a lack of surface-water flow at the present day, the topography of the Downs is characterized by extensive valley systems that were undoubtedly eroded by running water. They comprise two distinct forms. The southerly-facing dip slopes are dissected by extensive tributary valley systems that exhibit all the features of 'normal' valleys except they lack perennial streams. The upper valleys slope steeply and incise

© Peter Anderton (RIGS/SBRC)

Devil's Dyke, a large scarp-face valley or 'Coombe' that penetrates for over a kilometre into the Chalk. Note the straight, steep, straight-sided character of the valley slopes which contrast with the more rounded slopes of dip-slope valleys.

quite sharply, into the landscape often from just below the scarp crest. Most follow a rather sinuous course, gradually widening down-valley where the gradient of the floors lessen. In their mid-section the valley side slopes are often steep, but as the valleys widen the slopes generally become

gentler down-valley, although some maintain surprisingly steep slopes even along their lower stretches. The east-facing slope of Gap Bottom, as the valley descends from East Dean towards Birling Gap is a good example of one such steep slope.

In contrast to these extensive, winding dip-slope valleys, there are also shorter valleys that are incised into the scarp slope, the largest and most spectacular being Rake Bottom below Butser Hill and the Devil's Dyke north of Brighton. Most are much smaller, and several are little more than short, flat-floored linear recesses that penetrate into the scarp face for as little as 100–200 m or less backed by very steeply sloping, semi-circular rear walls. None have any real tributaries. Many have springs either within or a short distance beyond where they exit the scarp, although flow from some of these has lessened or ceased in recent times as a consequence of water-pumping stations that have been located within or nearby them. There is a continuum between what can clearly be called scarp 'valleys' in which the length is greater than their width and the frequent scallop-shaped hollows that dissect the scarp face, where incision has not produced a flat floor and the incision back into the scarp is equal to, or less than, the width of the hollow.

There has been considerable debate as to how and when both types of valleys were formed. Today, most incision is believed to date from cold periods of the Quaternary Ice Age when, under a periglacial climate

Flinty 'Coombe Rock' overlying frost-damaged Chalk exposed in the cliff at Birling Gap.

© David Robinson

with permafrost, all water within the Chalk would have frozen, making it impervious and consequently rain and meltwater in spring and summer would have flowed over the surface and carved the valleys. This would have been accentuated by freeze–thaw activity in the surface layers of the Chalk breaking up the rock, releasing flints and supplying erosive debris for transport by the water. Large quantities of this frost-shattered debris of Chalk and flint, known as 'Coombe Rock', still underlies the present dry valley floors and can be examined in detail along the coast of East Sussex where valleys are terminated as sea cliffs.

Between Brighton and Newhaven the valleys have all been at least partially obscured by sea-defences and associated urban development, but the deposits can still be accessed and viewed further east at Birling Gap, which survives in its natural state, and on a smaller scale at Hope Gap immediately east of Seaford Head.

Evidence suggests that some, but not all, of the scarp slope valleys may have formed in a very short period at the end of the last glacial period. The evidence comes, not from the South Downs but from a short valley called the Devil's Kneadingtrough on the North Downs near Brook in Kent where it has been possible to show that much of the material excavated from the valley was deposited on low land in front of the scarp over a period of only 1300 years between 12,800 and 11,500 years ago. However, there is evidence also that some other valleys originated at an earlier date. A particular feature of the two largest of the scarp valleys on the South Downs is that they both have sharp bends as they exit from the scarp. The cause of these has been much debated but is generally believed to reflect the joint patterns in the Chalk. Joints are likely to have been particularly susceptible to the freeze–thaw activity because water movement within the Chalk is concentrated along such lines.

Flowing water may have contributed to the creation of the dip slope valleys in particular, at times other than when the Chalk was frozen. There are good reasons to believe that in the past the water table within the Chalk may at times have been at a much higher elevation than at the present day, thereby facilitating more frequent water flow. For example, during past inter-glacial periods sea-level is known to have been relatively higher than it is today and this would have supported higher water levels in the Chalk. Over time, the clay vale to the north of the Downs has also been lowered significantly by erosion, lowering the elevation of the springs along the foot of the Chalk escarpment and thereby the water table within the Chalk. In the east, deepening of the river valleys that cut through the Chalk, especially during periods of low sea-level that accompanied the cold periods of the Ice Age will also have lowered the water table within the eastern Downs. Finally, it is known that the climate during the 10,000 years of the post-glacial period has at times been significantly wetter than at the present. More recently, over the past two centuries, extraction of water from the Chalk for water supply has further lowered groundwater levels, especially in dry years.

Historically, many dry valleys experienced annual water flows in winter, when the level of the water table rose to intersect the valley floors. These seasonal water flows gave the name 'bourne' to many valleys, but today only a few ever experience any significant flow, especially in the Eastern Downs, and then only in exceptionally wet periods in winter. A good example is the aptly named Winterbourne that descends eastwards from Falmer to Lewes and along whose valley the A27 trunk road has been built. Today, flow along the carriageway is diverted underground, but the road has a history of partial closure that has continued into very recent time, and the stream has also caused flooding in Lewes.

In the western Downs, the river Lavant which rises in the East Dean valley above Singleton and flows down to Chichester has, as its name might suggest, a more permanent flow. Nevertheless, it rises at different points along the valley according to the time of the year and how rainy it has been, and for much of the summer contains little or no flow. However, as with the Winterbourne it can have substantial flow and occasionally causes flooding in the lower-lying parts of Chichester through which it flows on its way to the sea. Further west, in Hampshire, the Downs have more surface water with the rivers Ems, Meon and Itchen all rising on and flowing through valleys within the Chalk. The greater and more permanent water flows as the Downs are traced westwards almost certainly relates to three factors. First, the more widespread occurrence of clay-rich Palaeogene deposits overlying the Chalk; second the increased distance from the sea and the height above sea-level of the junction between the Chalk and the overlying Palaeogene deposits that occupy the Coastal Plain and Hampshire Basin, and third the absence of deep river valleys cutting through the Chalk and helping to draw down the water table. Additionally, water extraction is lower in this region where populations are less and the area of Chalk outcrop greater.

A noticeable feature of the dip slope valley systems is how few break the line of the crest of the Downs. Most originate below the crest and are cut entirely into the dip slope. This suggests that the valleys are all relatively young and have developed whilst the crest was roughly in the same position as today. Chalk is known to be very susceptible to damage and destruction by freeze–thaw processes and extensive spreads of flint gravel cover low hilltops for several miles north of the Downs such as at Ambersham Common in West Sussex and towards Piltdown in East Sussex. These attest to the efficacy of frost attacking the Chalk scarp and releasing vast volumes of frost-shattered Chalk and flint that flowed down the scarp during summer snow melt. As a consequence the scarp must have retreated at a rapid rate. That the valleys appear to have developed since the crest was in approximately its present position suggests the majority of valleys have been created

© Peter Anderton (RIGS/SBRC)

South of Cocking the crest of the Downs is lowered by around 100 m by a wide dry valley that descends to the River Lavant at Singleton. This is believed to be the route of a former south-flowing river whose waters were 'captured' and diverted east by the River Rother.

mostly since the retreat of the scarp slowed or stopped at the end of the last period of very cold climate. This causes some conflict with the idea that they formed mostly under a periglacial climate when the Chalk was frozen. Perhaps they were eroded or deepened largely in the same short period at the end of the last ice age when the scarp valleys appear to have developed rapidly, or at least been extended.

Aerial view looking southeast along the A23 trunk road as it traverses the Pyecombe Gap north of Brighton. The highest point of this low-level, dry gap through the Chalk is approximately 80 metres lower than the crest of the scarp on either side.

Although the majority of dry downland valleys terminate below the summit ridge of the Downs, there are a few that lower the crest and are clearly remnants of earlier, longer valleys that flowed south from north of the current position of the scarp. Sometimes referred to as wind gaps, the largest and lowest is the Pyecombe Gap, through which the main A23 road and rail links between Brighton and London are routed. Of similar size is the Washington Gap through which the A24 traverses the Downs to the coast at Worthing. In the Western Downs, no river valley cuts through the Downs west of the Arun and all breaks in the scarp are high dry gaps, through which transport links are routed, the A325 south of Duncton, the A286 south of Cocking and the A3 and Portsmouth rail line south of Petersfield. The streams that cut these gaps must have flowed from the north, most probably when the Chalk cover extended further north, but they may also have drained parts of the underlying clays and sandstones when these rocks were first exposed by erosion stripping away the Chalk cover. In the east, some of these early streams flowing from north to south down the southern flanks of the original domed upland of southern England have managed to maintain their course and continue to flow through impressive valleys cut through the Chalk to the sea, but in the western portion of the Sussex Downs this is no longer the case. What appears to have happened is that the River Rother, a right bank tributary of the Arun, has eroded a valley along the soft silts and clays of the Sandgate Formation and cut off or 'captured' all the drainage coming from the north to divert it out via the Arun gap at Pulborough (see map on page i). Further east, the drainage that originally flowed south through the Washington, Pyecombe and Jevington gaps is believed to similarly have been captured by tributaries of the Arun, Adur and Ouse although the pattern is less clear.

A number of the flattish floors of dry valleys within the Downs have been excavated by scientists, including that of Devil's Dyke. The floors are not cut directly into the Chalk, but are underlain by a number of distinct deposits often several metres thick. Characteristically the lowest layers are comprised of flint-rich frost-shattered Chalk and silt. These are interpreted as the product of frost shattering and seasonal mass movement processes delivering material from the valley side slopes under a periglacial climate. The top 30 cm or so of this layer is often darker, sometimes quite blackish. This is a former soil with the dark colouration due to enrichment with organic matter. This soil is then buried by finer, chalky silt-rich material. Snail faunas recovered from the buried soil indicate a change from closed woodland to open habitat grass and shrub vegetation at the point where the soils were buried. The interpretation is that the buried soil developed under deciduous woodland that covered the Downs, and that clearance of the woodland by early farmers resulted in erosion of the valley sides and deposition at foot of the slopes which buried the soils in the valleys. Thus the thin soils that cover the slopes of the Downs today are the eroded remnants of thicker soils that once covered the landscape prior to woodland clearance by our Neolithic and later ancestors.

The sharp break in slope along the edge of many valleys is not a natural feature, but the result of past ploughing of the valley floors and the cutting of the plough share into the bottom of the slope. Sloping benches, sometimes forming broad steps on Downland slopes have a similar origin. Known as lynchets, these were cut by the ploughs of farmers from Romano-British to medieval times ploughing along

Soil erosion on the South Downs after heavy autumn rain. Erosion is restricted to bare or nearly bare arable fields and continues the thinning of soils on downland slopes that has occurred intermittently ever since their initial clearance for agriculture.

the slopes to grow crops when land was in short supply. Good examples can be found all across the Downs from slopes such as those above Jevington in the east to sites such as Catherington Down above Horndean in the west. Natural though the benches may appear today, especially when grassed over, or covered in shrubs, they are entirely a product of human use of the landscape, and indeed many have been lost since the middle of the 20th cen-tury by ploughing of slopes with modern, powerful agricultural machinery.

At the present day, short periods of rapid erosion of agricultural land still occasion-ally occur. They are mostly associated with periods of high intensity rain falling on largely unvegetated seed beds in autumn or spring. Local rates of soil loss can be considerable but most is re-distributed within valleys with the eroded soil depos-ited on valley floors immediately at the foot of eroded slopes, or within a few hundred metres or less from where it was eroded. Only small quantities are carried more than a kilometre and it is rare for the soil to be carried entirely out of the Downs. In the vicinity of Brighton, Hove and Lewes, urban development has occurred in the lower parts of some of these 'dry' valleys and eroded soil has been carried across the boundary of the Park and caused significant local flooding in some of these adjacent suburbs. The construction of the Brighton by-pass, which for much of its length lies close to the boundary of the Park, is today carried across several of the susceptible valleys on embankments which act as dams and this has reduced the risks of flooding in most of the northern suburbs of Brighton and Hove. Farming policies designed primarily to improve wildlife conservation on farms have also helped to reduce the incidence of such events.

When erosion occurs it is concentrated on the hillslopes and deposition occurs in the valley bottoms. This results in further thinning of the already thin soils on the slopes and thickening, of the richer soils in the valley bottoms – a continuation of the process that commenced with the first clearance of the Downs for agriculture. Erosion today tends to be concentrated along what are known as 'tramlines' along which tractors repeatedly cross fields during seedbed preparation, and later during applications of fertilizer, pesticides and weedkillers. In consequence, the soil becomes compacted and during rainfall events, rather than infiltrating into the soil, the rain runs off over the surface, eroding rills and gullies. Often these are only tens of millimeters deep, but in extreme events can exceed a metre. The flows of water are sufficient not only to erode the fine soil but to carry also large flints down to the valley floors. In severe events the rills and gullies actually erode into the underlying Chalk, the upper parts of which are often extensively fissured by past frost action.

The Chalk Downs also suffer erosion by loss in solution. Rainwater falling on the Downs and draining into the Chalk dissolves the rock through which it drains. Most of the solution occurs close to the surface because the water very quickly becomes saturated with calcium once it enters the Chalk. It has been estimated that the annual loss through solution is of the order of 60 m^3 km^2 per year, which equates to a surface lowering of 60 mm

Gullies can erode through the entire soil layer and into the Chalk.

In extreme cases soil erosion can cut gullies a metre or more in depth. Fine material is carried off the fields, but most of the flint stones are carried only a short distance before deposition.

per 1000 years. In reality, because water movement through the Chalk occurs preferentially along joints and fissures, the lowering will have been more selective and not equal over the area of the Chalk outcrop. Nevertheless, although this rate

of lowering may seem small in human life spans, in geological time it is very considerable and may account for surface lowering of up to 200 metres or more over the period since parts of the Chalk were first exposed.

© David Robinson

© David Robinson

© David Robinson

The famous spring at Fulking emerging from the garden of the 'Shepherd and Dog' public house. The flow from such scarp-foot springs remains remarkably strong even during dry summer weather.

Historically many scarp-foot springs were dammed and harnessed for water power. Today many of the former mill ponds remain as decorative features in the gardens of private houses.

Many springs emerge in mini-gorges overgrown with vegetation and the water often emerges from several points, such as here at Duncton Mill.

Chalk springs

A large proportion of the rainwater that soaks into the Chalk emerges at springs. The most impressive of these lie at the foot of the Chalk scarp, which at intervals is marked by a series of strong, gushing springs that have a remarkably constant flow even in dry summer weather. They are particularly frequent in the west of West Sussex where there are some 15 major springs between Petersfield and the Adur gap. Here, the Downs are further from the sea, there is an absence of low river valleys where water drains out of the Chalk and pumping for water supply is less intense. Many actually emerge, not from the Chalk, but from the base of the underlying, porous Upper Greensand malmstone, which is well

The rivers flowing in large flat-floored valleys through the Downs flood quite frequently during very wet weather as can be seen here in the Ouse valley.

© David Robinson

of the Devil's Dyke. East of Lewes, scarp foot springs are sparse.

The scarp foot springs flow from the same location throughout the year and many emerge at the base of armchair-shaped hollows with a vertical or near vertical rear face of Chalk or malmstone several metres in height. Incision and retreat of the spring head, a process known as 'sapping', has often left a mini-gorge immediately downstream, frequently heavily overgrown and usually only a few tens of metres in length, but occasionally longer. The exact roles of different processes of stream erosion, bank undermining and slope collapse that contribute to spring sapping are variable in effect and rather poorly understood, but solution is unlikely to be important because the water is saturated in calcium long before it emerges at the springs. The rapid movement of water within the Chalk that feeds the springs occurs along major joints and fissures which are also zones of weakness within the Chalk. Water movement along these pathways further widens the joints, but probably of greater importance was the impact of periglacial freeze–thaw activity. This would have been greatest where the Chalk was saturated and therefore accentuated shattering and breakup

developed along this stretch of the Downs. A very good example that can be easily viewed from a public right of way is one that feeds Duncton Mill. Here, as at many of the springs, the flow of water was harnessed in the past with a small dam and pond to provide water power. Many of these now form decorative features in the gardens of private houses, several of which are converted

mills. Although less frequent, there are still many powerful springs further east. Two famous examples that can easily be visited are at Edburton and Fulking, at the foot of the scarp north of Brighton. The latter feeds a stream that flows through the garden of the 'Shepherd and Dog' public house and then alongside the road. Another emerges adjacent to the footpath in the lower part

© Ben du Boulay

The valleys of the rivers that flow through the Chalk are very large compared to the size of the rivers. Such 'misfits' indicate that the rivers were once much larger than they are today.

rise to no marked feature. This is for a combination of reasons. The springs emerge generally on the flat floors of the valleys rather than at the foot of steep slopes and there is no slope where sapping can occur. They are less permanent, and the locations where the springs arise vary according to where the height of the water table in the Chalk intersects the valley floor. This rises and falls seasonally, normally being at its highest in late winter/early spring. At present many springs flow only in exceptionally wet years, and the flows are often short-lived, sometimes only a matter of days, rarely more than a few weeks.

The river gaps

The rivers that flow through the eastern Downs have wide flat-floored valleys, that lie at, or only a little above sea-level. Although some sections are several kilometres upstream from the coast, the rivers are all tidal and prone to flood during periods of wet weather. In winter, flood water can remain on parts of the land surface for several weeks. Compared to the valleys in which they flow, the rivers are quite small. In other words, there is a 'misfit' between the size of the rivers and the size of the valleys. This misfit applies also to the bends in the valley sides and the bends or 'meanders'

of the Chalk in the vicinity of the joints. Many springs lie below the scallop-shaped indents in the scarp face, or are located in the short scarp foot valleys or coombs that penetrate the scarp face, such as that which rises in the Devil's Dyke north of Brighton. All evidence indicates that these are also the result of preferential damage by freeze–thaw processes along the same

joints. Spreads of periglacial, frost-derived head deposits often emerge from these scarp face coombs and spring head embayments.

In contrast, most of the ephemeral springs in dip slope dry valley systems are rather different in character. The water mostly seeps or bubbles to the surface and gives

of the rivers as they flow through the valleys. This can be observed very clearly from maps and the air, and also from high vantage points on the valley sides. Good places include the magnificent viewpoint of 'High and Over' on the west side of the Cuckmere, and Mount Caburn or the top of the road leading to the Lewes Golf Club high above the Ouse. Public viewpoints over the Adur and Arun are rather more distant and not so good. To improve drainage, and protect from flooding, the rivers are extensively canalized with artificial embankments or 'levees' constructed along their banks and several bends within the rivers have been cut off. This includes the very famous meanders in the Lower Cuckmere, immediately south of Exceat Bridge; a large one at Hamsey immediately north of Lewes and a smaller one at Piddinghoe on the Ouse, and two extremely large ones at Burpham and South Stoke on the Arun.

These low-lying valleys are floored with poorly drained, silt-rich alluvium. Ground water lies at or close to the ground surface for much of the year, and water stands on the surface in winter. Even in summer the ground-water level rarely falls more than a metre below the surface. The resulting soils are extensively waterlogged alluvial gleys.

© David Robinson

In the past, before the rivers flowing through the Downs were constrained by artificial banks or 'levees', flooding of the lower reaches of their valleys was more frequent than today, and remnants of the old channels that drained the surrounding marshland, such as here along the Lower Cuckmere, can still be seen.

Uniformly fine-grained in texture, they are greyish-brown in colour at the surface, but are heavily mottled grey and yellow below the surface because of the waterlogging. In the past, natural drainage was so poor that peat formed in some areas, but today active peat growth has mostly ceased because of embanking of the rivers, ditching and artificial drainage. Nevertheless, problems of flooding and poor drainage restrict agricultural usage to pasture, except where artificial drainage allows the cultivation of some arable crops. When drained the soils are fertile, and potentially of high value

© Airscapes.co.uk

As they pass through the Downs, the Sussex rivers exhibit large meanders as they flow across very flat-floored valleys. Over the centuries, many meanders, such as these on the Lower Cuckmere, have been bypassed to improve drainage and navigation.

if the threat of periodic flooding can be removed.

The flat floors of the valleys hide deeper valleys cut into the rock beneath. These deep valleys were eroded during the cold periods of the Quaternary when sea-level was lowered as a result of sea water contracting in volume, due to the low temperatures, and because of the build-up of ice which stored vast quantities of water on the continental landmasses. At the maximum of the last glacial period, around 18,000 years ago, sea-level was probably 130–140 m below its present level. The bed of the English Channel was dry land and the nearest coastline lay well west of the British mainland. As a consequence, the south-flowing rivers incised and steepened their channels, cutting down to well below present-day sea-level. Within the Park, the rock floor of the Arun valley at Arundel, for example lies at −36 m below the current valley floor, the Adur between Bramber and Shoreham around −20 m and the Ouse −12 m at Lewes descending to −30 m at its mouth just south of the Park boundary. The rock floor of the Cuckmere in the vicinity of Exceat Bridge is below −13 m and at its mouth is believed to be below −20 m.

The Amberley Wildbrooks in the Arun valley occupies an area underlain by peat that still floods regularly today. Plans to drain the area in the 1970s were stopped and it is now a valued wetland for wildlife.

© David Robinson

The old cliff line, now degraded and wooded, that developed on the east side of the Ouse estuary when it was open to the sea, is skirted by the A259 between Denton and Seaford.

As the climate warmed at the end of the Ice Age, sea-level rose rapidly, reaching the present coastline around 5000 years ago and attaining its present level, or a very slightly higher level, by 3000 years ago. The rivers became more sluggish and began to deposit a complex sequence of gravels, sands, silts and clays, interbedded in places with peats that appear to have accumulated in riverside swamps. Eventually the rising sea gradually flooded the lower valleys turning them progressively into tidal estuaries over the period from 5000–3000 years ago. Marine silts and clays replaced freshwater deposits, but deposition was slow, and whilst the upper reaches of the estuaries began to fill in quite quickly with river-borne silts, clays and peat that overlie the marine sediments. The lower valleys remained as open estuaries certainly into Romano-British times and probably into the Norman period. The mouths of the estuaries were sufficiently open for cliffs to be cut in the Chalk around the southwest-facing margins of the Ouse and Cuckmere, exposed to the prevailing direction of wind and waves. One of these now degraded cliff lines is particularly well developed just inside the southern margin of the Park between Denton and Bishopstone where the A259 skirts along its base. Studies here of a fossil beach at the foot of the cliff indicate that the site was still open to full marine conditions around 2500–2000 years ago.

Whilst historically the subsequent management of these rivers has focused on speeding the flow of water to the sea along canalized channels, the priorities in the 21st century are changing. With increased leisure time, improved means of personal transport and better standards of education, society increasingly values environmental quality over maximization of agricultural production. As a consequence, expensive management of these valleys to prevent flooding and maintain them as farmland is becoming less fashionable. It is recognized increasingly that speeding the flow of water off agricultural land through drainage leads to higher peak flows in the rivers, which actually increases the likeli-

Pulborough Brooks, in the Arun valley, is an important wetland reserve for birds managed by the RSPB.

hood of flooding, especially of vulnerable towns such as Lewes. Further, allowing controlled overbank flooding and storage of water on agricultural floodplains where it can do no damage is an effective flood prevention measure to protect areas where uncontrolled flooding causes disruption and damage. Because of widespread drainage in the latter part of the 20th century, wetlands became a threatened habitat in Britain, and reversion of river management to a more natural regime of flooding to restore this habitat has become a high priority. Nowhere is this priority being better addressed at a variety of scales than on the flood plains of the rivers within the Park. This is especially true of the Arun, with the large RSPB Reserve at Pulborough Brooks and the smaller reserve managed by the Sussex Wildlife Trust at Greatham Bridge.

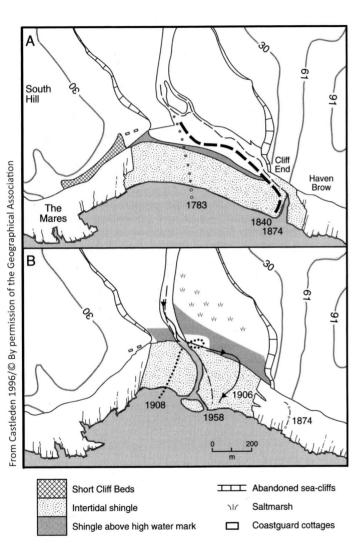

A

South
Hill

The
Mares

Cliff
End

Haven
Brow

1783

1840
1874

B

1908

1906

1958

1874

0   200
m

Short Cliff Beds

Intertidal shingle

Shingle above high water mark

Abandoned sea-cliffs

Saltmarsh

Coastguard cottages

Changes in the position of the mouth of the River Cuckmere as shown on maps since the late 18th century. Shingle drifting from west to east along the south coast obstructs the mouths of rivers, diverting them eastwards. During storms the shingle bars are sometimes breached creating a new mouth. Engineers have also re-cut river mouths to improve drainage in the valleys and access to river ports.

More controversial are plans to restore large parts of the valley of the lower Cuckmere, south of Exceat Bridge, to a more natural state. This will involve breaching the current levees alongside the river to allow the land to flood during high tides. The result will be to change the current grazing land into mud-flats and saltmarsh that will, over time, accrete naturally. This will reverse many centuries of reclamation, but retaining such areas as grassland when sea-level is rising is becoming increasingly uneconomic and it will create a valuable wetland habitat for wildlife. Thus entering the 21st century we are seeing a move away from engineering the physical environment to create a economically valuable agricultural landscape to one in which we increasingly allow natural processes to re-assert themselves and enable the physical landscape to evolve more naturally for the benefit of wildlife and conservation.

The final silting up of the river estuaries was assisted by the growth of shingle spits across the mouths of the rivers. Only one of these lies within the Park, across the mouth of the Cuckmere, and no longer looks much like a spit because, like others along the Sussex coast, it has been artificially cut through to speed the exit of river

The mouth of the Cuckmere looking east. The groynes constraining the mouth have now been removed and drifting shingle is diverting the mouth eastwards.

© David Robinson

© Peter Anderton (RIGS/SBRC)

Rapid rates of retreat and strong vertical joints within the Chalk help to maintain characteristically vertical cliffs as seen here between Cuckmere Haven and Birling Gap.

Caves such as this one at Telscombe are relatively rare along the Sussex coast. They tend to develop along weaknesses in the Chalk such as vertical joints or where the rock is fissured.

water and assist drainage and reclamation of land within the valley. Waves generally approach the Sussex coast from the south-west and move beach material eastwards along the shore. The dominant material on the Sussex coast is flint shingle derived originally from the Chalk. This led to the growth of shingle spits from the western margins, across the mouths of the Sussex estuaries. Exactly when the spit across the

Cuckmere began to form is largely conjecture, but by the time the first reliable map of the Sussex coast was produced in 1587 the mouth is shown deflected against the eastern edge of the valley adjacent to Cliff End by a spit. This would have made the river behind very sluggish and accentuated deposition of sediment behind the spit rather than in the sea. Periodically, as the river mouth became increasingly

blocked during storms, the river broke through the spit to re-establish an exit further west. Thus in 1783 it appears to have been in the centre very close to where it is today, but a century later in the 1874 it was back in the east below Cliff End. In the early 20th century it was again more central, and throughout the latter half of the 20th century it is was stabilized in this position, artificially held in position by

Sea stacks, resistant masses of rock left behind when the cliff retreats, such as this one east of Seaford, are extremely rare along the Sussex coast.

metal training groynes. In recent years, as part of the scheme to 're-naturalize' the lower valley, these restraining groynes have been removed and shingle drifting across the mouth is once again creating a spit, currently visible only at low tide, that is diverting the river mouth eastwards.

The Chalk coast

Between Brighton and Eastbourne, the Chalk outcrop is terminated by impressive sea cliffs that frequently exceed 60 m in height and reach over 150 m at Beachy Head. The cliffs are vertical or near vertical throughout and their continuity is broken

only by the two wide river mouths of the Ouse and Cuckmere. Towards their base, the cliffs sometimes exhibit slight undercutting and there are a few short caves that penetrate the cliff face. Detached stacks left by retreat of the cliffs are extremely rare. From the Ouse gap eastwards, the cliffs are

© Tony Wilson

The magnificent Chalk cliffs east of Brighton were trimmed back and protected by a sea wall in the 1930s which has recently been reconstructed. Where dry valleys reach the coast, the cliffs are lower and urban development has occurred.

entirely unprotected and all lie within the Park, but west of here urban development has been allowed on the cliff-top and large sections are protected at their base by a sea wall and concrete platform. Only a short stretch of this protected cliff, between Rottingdean and Brighton Marina, actually lies within the Park.

Over the past hundred years or so the unprotected cliffs have been retreating at an average of about 0.35 m per year. This retreat is variable in space and time, with some sections retreating at an average of over 1.0 m per year. Retreat is caused by the combined action of rain, frost and salt and the pounding of waves at the foot of the cliffs. It is concentrated in winter, especially during gales when wave pounding is most intense and the Chalk above is heavy because it is saturated with water, and immediately following cold frosty weather when ice developed within the Chalk thaws. The cliffs seem particularly vulnerable to collapse if such winter weather follows very dry summers when vertical fissures often develop behind the cliff faces. If the current rates of erosion were representative of those that occurred throughout historic times the coast would have been 0.5 to 2.0 km seaward of its present position when the Romans arrived, but other evidence suggests this was not the case and rates appear to have varied over time.

The most frequent cause of retreat is the mass failure and collapse of short slices of cliff face, commonly involving stretches of only a few metres. The cliff top retreats by only a metre or so, releasing 1000–2000 m³ of Chalk, sometimes less, which forms a cone of debris at the foot of the cliff. This temporarily protects the base of the cliff from further attack by the sea

© Peter Anderton (RIGS/SBRC)

A typical small cliff fall. Note how failure lines clearly relate to joints in the rock face and how the debris forms a small cone at the cliff foot.

© David Robinson

Debris of the large cliff fall at Beachy Head in 1999 when it is estimated between 100,000 and 150,000 m³ of Chalk collapsed into the sea.

until waves have removed the debris. Fine debris is removed very rapidly, but larger debris can take several years. In places, arcs of larger boulder can be identified on the foreshore, marking the outer margins of debris cones from past collapses. More rarely much larger collapses occur that result in stretches of cliff tens of metres in length retreating by several metres and involve the collapse of several tens of thousands of cubic metres of Chalk. Some of these run out at the base of the cliff, across the foreshore for tens of metres to, or below, the position of the lowest low tides. The largest of these in recent years

In very cold weather freezing of the cliff face can cause severe damage, which becomes apparent when thawing occurs and debris falls from the cliff face as here at Saltdean in the winter of 1986/7 when temperatures dropped as low as −10°C.

A small cobble of Chalk with holes bored by Piddocks. This cobble will have broken off the lower part of the Chalk platform since when it has become rounded and the holes enlarged by wave action.

(Left) Aerial view of the cliffs east of Birling Gap. Note the arc of debris from a fresh cliff fall below the old Belle Tout Lighthouse and the arc of discoloured boulders further east marking an older fall. The lighthouse was originally built 33 metres from the cliff edge in 1832. In 1999 it was so threatened by cliff retreat that it was jacked up and rolled back a further 17 metres.

was at Beachy Head, where in 1999 it is estimated that between 100,000–150,000 m³ of Chalk collapsed and the debris apron stretched seaward across the foreshore towards the lighthouse for 115 m. It takes decades for the sea to remove such large volumes of debris and for it to once again attack the cliff from where such large falls occurred. For example, at the time of writing, a substantial quantity of the apron from the 1999 collapse at Beachy Head has still to be removed. The features of

individual cliff collapses, their dimensions and the volume, shape and character of the debris produced is influenced also by the variation in properties such as cementation, joint and fracture patterns of the different beds of Chalk involved in a collapse.

In addition to large mass collapse of cliffs, small, discrete pieces of the cliff face also periodically fall away as a result of freeze–thaw, salt weathering, and expansion and contraction caused by heating and cooling

Retreat of the Chalk cliffs leaves behind inter-tidal shore platforms that are drained by shallow channels or 'runnels' along which water movement and erosion is concentrated as the tide rises and fall.

or wetting and drying. Very little is known about the loss of such material in terms of the volumes involved either on an annual or seasonal basis, but in most years the volumes of material lost, when averaged over the entire cliff face, are low. However in very cold winters when the entire face can freeze to considerable depth, considerable volumes are released on thawing, sufficient, for example, for the walkways

below the cliffs east from Brighton to have to be closed for safety reasons.

Extensive shore platforms extend seaward from the cliff foot for up to 200 m or more to below the low tide position. The upper part of the platform is sometimes covered by a shingle beach of varying depth and volume, but the remainder of the platform comprises Chalk with a variable cover of

sea weed. In many areas the platform is bare to the foot of the cliff where it sometimes curves smoothly upwards into the cliff face. Elsewhere the junction between the cliff and the platform is more angular and sometimes stepped. The platforms slope seawards at a very gentle average angle of 3–4°, sometimes as a continuously smooth surface but elsewhere as a series of irregular steps up to a metre or more

© David Robinson

© David Robinson

Examples of the severe damage caused by frost to Chalk shore platforms during extremely cold weather. *(Left)* Spalling of the upper surface the shore platform. *(Right)* Breakage and collapse of the face of a platform step or riser.

in height. The steps are often the depth of rock between individual bedding planes and sometimes they are capped by a band of flint. The surfaces of the platforms are frequently dissected by systems of channels or 'runnels' eroded into the Chalk that deepen and sometimes widen seaward. Water is channeled along the runnels during the rise and fall of the tide carrying sand, shingle and cobbles that abrade their sides and floor. At the seaward end most platforms are terminated by a large step or low

cliff that is rarely if ever exposed by even the lowest tides.

Formed by the retreat of the cliffs at their rear, shore platforms reduce the energy of waves reaching the cliffs. For cliff retreat to continue it must therefore be accompanied by erosion of the platform. Lowering of the platform surface and backwearing of the steps occurs through a variety of processes. The surface is lowered by wave action and abrasion by sediment moved by the waves.

This is especially effective in a zone immediately below any shingle beach, and in runnels, where the Chalk displays a very smooth, white, abraded surface. Biological organisms such as limpets abrade the surface whilst grazing and aid solution of the underlying Chalk with their secretions. Some organisms such as Piddocks bore tunnels into the rock, not only removing Chalk directly, but also weakening it for attack by other processes. Cobbles and boulders of Chalk full of holes bored by Piddocks can often be found on the platforms and beaches. Solution, and wetting and drying in the presence of salts weaken the surface of the platforms, which in calm weather can become soft and slimy. In subsequent stormy weather the sea often turns milky with suspended particles of Chalk removed from the platform. Elsewhere, some platforms exhibit a very sharp micro-topography of hollows and pinnacles that is thought to result from differential solution of the Chalk surface. In very cold weather, the entire surface of the platforms can be extensively damaged by frost action which in combination with salt causes significant cracking and spalling of the Chalk, especially on those areas exposed longest between tides and on the upper edges of runnels and steps where freezing can penetrate from two directions. Occasionally freeze–thaw can lead to the collapse of entire sections of step face. Wave action and the impact of cobbles and shingle abrade the steps and break off pieces of Chalk from the faces. Entire joint bound blocks often

(Top right) The famous Seven Sisters where cliff retreat has terminated a series of dry valleys causing them to 'hang' above present day sea-level.

(Bottom right) The Seven Sisters are the brows of the hills separated by valleys that hang at differing heights above the sea.

© David Robinson

From Castleden 1996/© By permission of the Geographical Association

become detached and gradually break down at the foot of the step, but occasionally they are thrown up onto the platform surface where they can remain for several years.

Platform erosion is greatest in winter, especially during storms or very cold periods. Because the incidence of storms and the severity of frosts vary significantly from winter to winter, erosion of the platforms also varies from year to year. Measurements suggest average rates of lowering of the platform surface are of the order of 2.5–3.5 mm per year. The retreat of the steps is spatially very variable and difficult to measure but the volume of Chalk lost each year by this process seems to be similar to that lost by downwearing.

In front of the section of sea wall between Rottingdean and Brighton Marina, a landward-facing step can be observed on the platform some ten metres or so from the wall. This is the product of damage caused close to the platform by heavy machinery during the construction and repair of the wall, and the erosive energy of waves that are reflected back to sea after hitting the wall. This phenomenon can be seen at a number of locations in front of this protective wall, most of which lies outside the

Park. Accelerated lowering of the platform and incision of runnels can be observed also alongside the remnants of groynes that have protected the surface on which they were built from the 1930s onwards.

The cliffs along this Chalk coastline cut across a series of short dry valleys, the floors of which lie at varying heights above the present day sea-level. The most famous are the hanging valleys with intervening rounded crests that form the famous switchback profile of the Seven Sisters between the Cuckmere Haven and Birling Gap. These short valleys once extended seaward and when sea-level rose as the climate ameliorated at the end of the last cold period of the Ice Age, the coastline would have been indented with the valleys forming inlets between headlands formed by the crests. However, in the absence of streams to continue downcutting of the valleys, shoreline retreat by marine erosion has straightened the coastline and created cliffs that now truncate the valleys and left them 'hanging' tens of metres above present sea-level. The larger valleys descend closest to sea-level, the largest, Gap Bottom, exiting at Birling Gap, just 12 m above present day sea-level, whilst the shortest, known appropriately as Short Bottom, exits approximately 60 m above sea-level.

Birling Gap is a very important site because it provides the only remaining undisturbed cross section of a low-level valley emerging from the Chalk. The cliff is cut in periglacial Coombe Rock deposits underlain by frost shattered in situ Chalk. The Coombe Rock comprises a mixture of frost-shattered Chalk and flint embedded in a fine, biscuit coloured loessial silt and chalky mud. This passes downwards into Chalk that has also been shattered and disturbed by frost action. This disturbance can be seen clearly if one tries to follow the bands of flint which become irregular and broken as they pass below the floor of the valley. The Chalk is damaged to below the high water line and the shore platform below the cliffs is much lower than that developed in sound Chalk on either side. The axis of the valley and the lowered platform runs south eastward as it is traced down-shore, rather than running out at a right-angle to the cliff. Other similar valley sections that existed further west at Saltdean, Rottingdean and Ovingdean are today all partially obscured by public access routes and associated urban development.

A section across a much smaller, hanging dry valley can be viewed at Hope Gap, between Cuckmere Haven and Seaford Head, where there is access to the shore down steps

© David Robinson

© David Robinson

The cliffs below the valley floor at Birling Gap show flinty Coombe Rock overlying Chalk that has been badly shattered by deep freeze–thaw processes that operated under periglacial conditions in the Quaternary. Flint bands within the Chalk remain visible, but have been contorted by the frost action.

Beach gravel mostly comprises a mixture of grey and brown flint pebbles. The grey pebbles have been eroded directly from the Chalk and rounded by marine action. The brown pebbles were initially eroded from the Chalk long ago and then incorporated into Palaeogene or later geological deposits, where they became indelibly stained with iron, before further erosion released them on to present-day beaches.

(Left) Birling Gap where a low-level dry valley terminates at a low cliff. Frost damage to the Chalk in the valley floor descends below present day sea-level and as a consequence there is no shore platform offshore of the valley axis. The three most seaward of the terrace of eight cottages in the foreground, built in 1878, have had to be demolished in the past 40 years because of rapid cliff retreat.

from a short dry valley known as Hope Bottom, that descends from a car park at South Hill Barn. A small cross section of valley deposits can be inspected to the west of the steps. Here, a brown sandy silt, derived by erosion from the loess-clothed hillsides above, sits on frost-damaged Chalk below

the valley floor. This frost-damaged Chalk is more easily eroded than the sounder Chalk to either side, and the former seaward extension of the valley can be traced running offshore as a large embayment in the shore platform below the cliffs.

Hope Gap provides access also to excellent sections in the Sussex White Chalk, a shore platform and examples of well-developed pipes of superficial material let down into the Chalk that are cross-sectioned by the present cliff (see p. 47).

Beaches along the coast are composed predominantly of flint gravel. There are two quite distinct types of flint. Some are well rounded, and predominantly pale brown or beige in colour. Others are predominantly grey or mottled grey and white. Many of the latter are also are well rounded but some are more irregular in shape, although with edges that are generally smooth and rounded. Occasionally they may have sharp, freshly broken edges. These predominantly grey flints are derived directly from the Chalk and are the resistant residue of marine erosion of the cliffs and platforms, left behind when the softer Chalk has been broken down and washed away by the waves. The browner flints were also derived from the Chalk, but many millions of years ago. After having been rolled and battered by past seas they were incorporated into the Palaeogene deposits, during when they became stained with iron, and from where they have since been re-excavated by erosion. Many flints are believed to have been carried up to the present shoreline from out in the English Channel as sea-level rose in the post-glacial period. Some of these were probably derived from Chalk that outcrops on the floor of the English Channel, but others were initially released from the Chalk by periglacial processes during, for example, the erosion of the dry valleys. They were transported out of the Downs and deposited in large fans on the floor of the Channel, below present-day sea-level. They have since been re-worked by marine action and carried up onto the present beaches as sea-level rose.

Thus, the gravel on beaches within the Park is largely a fossil resource that is not being replenished at the present day. The annual supply of flint from cliff erosion is small and much smaller than it used to be. Beach gravel along the Sussex coast is driven eastwards by the prevailing winds and waves that arrive from the southwest. Historically, flint arrived along the shore now included within the Park from the shore to the west, beyond the Park boundary, derived by erosion from both the Chalk cliffs and the low lying coast of West Sussex. Today, this entire area is protected from erosion by sea-walls and other coastal defences. Beaches are groyned, and there are major breakwaters at Shoreham Harbour, Brighton Marina and Newhaven that trap gravel and stop most of it migrating east to the Park coast. There is also extensive recycling of beach gravel at places such as Seaford designed to maintain beach levels.

Beach gravel within the Park is free to move under the influence of wind and waves and beach volumes vary significantly over time, especially during storms. The beach at Birling Gap for example has been known to disappear entirely during storms, although it quickly rebuilds and overall appears to have changed little in volume over the past century. In general, beaches are drawn down by storms and are built up during calmer conditions. At Cuckmere Haven, gravel was for many years trapped on the west side of restraining walls protecting the river mouth, and some of the gravel that accumulated as an inter-tidal delta, where the river entered the sea, was re-cycled to help maintain the height and width of the beach west of the river to lessen the risk of a breach occurring that would flood the land behind. However, as part of the scheme to allow the lower Cuckmere valley to return to a more natural state, this has now ceased and eastward drifting gravel is building a new spit that is again diverting the river mouth to the east.

Sea-level change

At the present day, sea-level along the Sussex coast is rising at 3–4 mm per year. This is the result of a globally rising sea-level resulting from a warming climate, and the fact that southern England is slowly sinking. During past Quaternary interglacial warm periods, sea-level along the Sussex coast appears to have reached locations that today are considerably above present sea-level. A sequence of old beach deposits comprising sands and gravels, each resting on a beveled platform backed by a degraded cliff line, can be traced across the Sussex Coastal Plain, buried under younger deposits of re-worked loess and fans of flint-rich gravels from the Downs. The full sequence is best developed west of the river Arun, where the highest cliff and platform is cut into the dip slope of the Downs at elevations between 32 and 43 m above present sea-level. Evidence comes from sand and gravel quarries, especially around Slindon and Boxgrove, which have today ceased working. At least four younger, buried beaches at lower elevations lie to the south, the lowest comprising gravels that are exposed in low cliffs at Selsey Bill at an elevation of only 2–3 m above present sea-level. The origin of this staircase of beaches, particularly the higher, is prob-

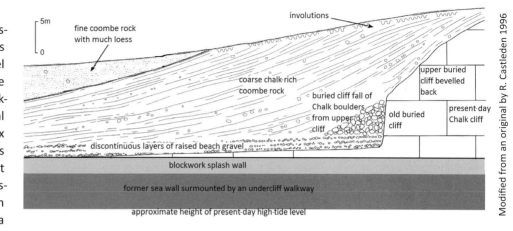

Modified from an original by R. Castleden 1996

A diagram of the cliff at Black Rock, Brighton where a raised beach can be seen resting on a shore platform. The beach is backed against a former cliff that intersects the present cliff at an oblique angle. The platform relates to a former inter-glacial sea-level *c.* 8 m above present-day sea-level and the rear of the beach reaches *c.* 12 m. The raised beach and former cliff are buried beneath many metres of silt-rich Chalk and flint debris resulting from frost action and slope processes acting on the Downs above during subsequent periods of cold, periglacial conditions. The sea no longer reaches this section of cliff or cliff wall because of the construction of Brighton Marina. There is an interpretation board at the western end of the section, on the undercliff walkway. The horizontal scale of the diagram is compressed – the section is *c.* 100 metres in length.

lematic because there is little evidence of a progressive global fall in sea-level of this magnitude during the Quaternary. It is therefore considered probable that southern Sussex has been slowly uplifted over this period, despite apparently sinking at the present day.

Further east, where the coastal plain narrows as the Chalk approaches the present coast, evidence of the higher of the beaches is absent, probably lost to marine erosion during the cutting of lower platforms in later interglacial periods. The main platform surviving in this region lies 7–8 m

© Geoffrey Mead

The raised beach and associated deposits at Black Rock, Brighton, viewed from the undercliff walkway, showing *(left)* raised beach gravel backed against and partially underlying frost-shattered remnants of the old Chalk cliff, all buried beneath silt-rich periglacial slope deposits; and *(right)* detail of the beach gravel intermixed with broken blocks of Chalk lying on a platform of Chalk stretching away from the old cliff.

above present sea-level, on which lies a gravel beach of rounded flints with a little sand reaching to about 12 m and at the rear, a fossil cliff. This fossil cliff and raised beach meets the present cliffs obliquely at Black Rock, at the rear of the northwest corner of Brighton Marina, just outside the Park boundary. Here, the eastern section of the raised gravel beach, abutting the fossil

cliff, is first overlain by angular Chalk blocks which are believed to have fallen onto the beach as a result of frost acting on the cliff above, and then the entire raised platform and beach stretching westwards is buried beneath tens of metres of loess-rich flint and Chalk debris, with occasional sarsens, that came over the cliff from the downland slopes and valley behind, completely bury-

ing the entire fossil cliff. This buried cliff line and associated deposits can be traced westwards from here through the centre of Brighton and Hove across the coastal plain to Chichester and beyond. In earlier centuries, remnants of the raised beach could be traced east of Black Rock as far as Rottingdean, but these have all now been lost due to cliff retreat.

The scenery of the Western Weald

Those areas of the Park in West Sussex that are underlain by the predominantly sandy and silty Greensand formations and the Gault and Weald clays, display a markedly contrasting landscape to that of the Chalk Downs. The region is strongly influenced by local anticlinal flexures subsidiary to the main Wealden axis of uplift across central Sussex and Kent. In the vicinity of Fernhurst, the Hythe Formation, reinforced by chert, forms impressively high in-facing escarpments, that reach 207 m in the south at Telegraph Hill and 280 m in the north at Blackdown, overlooking the Vale of Fernhurst, which mostly lies at between 75 and 85 m. Throughout the vale, the in-facing escarpments are never more than 4 km apart and wonderful views across the vale to the opposing scarp can be obtained from viewpoints on the scarp crests at Blackdown, Bexley Hill, Henley and Telegraph Hill. Views along the vale at the impressive in-facing scarps can be obtained from Harting Coombe in the west and on a clear day from high points on the Downs to the east such as Kithurst Hill and Chantry Hill above Storrington.

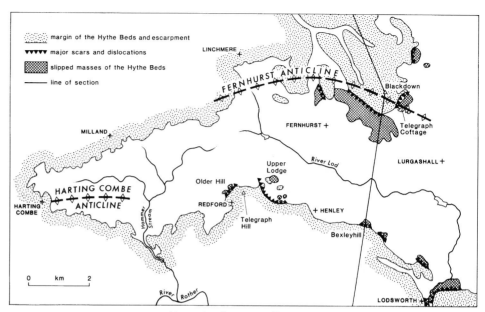

Robinson & Williams 1984/© By permission of the Geographical Association

Map of the Vale of Fernhurst showing the two major anticlinal structures that have been breached to expose the Weald Clay below, and the in-facing escarpments of Hythe Formation sandstone beds with major landslips along the scarp faces.

This dramatic topography is the result of what is known as anticlinal breaching. Two east–west trending anticlines run through the vale. In the east, the Fernhurst Anticline runs along the northern edge of the vale, and 2 to 3 km to the southwest the Harting Coombe Anticline lies at the head of the vale. Following uplift these would have been the areas of highest relief. However, subsequent erosion has removed the younger rocks, including the Hythe Formation to expose and excavate the soft Atherfield and Weald clays beneath. Thus what was an area of structurally uplifted land is today an area of low ground, another excellent example of inverted relief (see also the example of

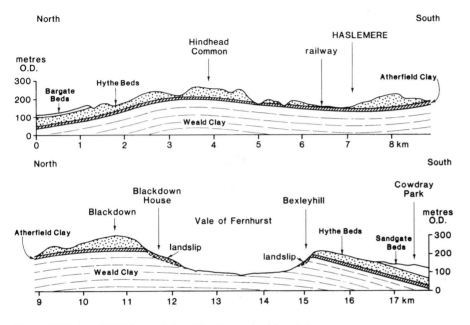

Robinson & Williams 1984/© By permission of the Geographical Association

Section across the Vale of Fernhurst along the line shown on the map (p. 89), illustrating the structure with the breached cap of Hythe Formation sandstone beds dipping away to the north and south.

the Vale of Brooks, pp. 53–4). In the west the vale is closed where the north- and south-facing escarpments formed by the sandstones in the Hythe Formation come together at Harting Coombe. This western end of the vale has been excavated by the Hammer Stream which escapes southwards into the Rother through a breach in the southern escarpment south of Milland. In the east the vale has been opened up to join the Weald Clay vale by the easterly flowing River Lod, which then turns southwards to cut through the Hythe Formation between Lodsworth and River, where chert reinforcing of the sandstones is less and the escarpment much lower.

At the top of the escarpments, the individual beds of rock can be seen to bend over the crest and the joints are often open, with some blocks having moved apart and rotated on their base to produce very variable dips. This is a process known as cambering and is believed to be a fossil feature that developed during the Quaternary Ice Ages. During each intense cold period, the clays underlying the sandstones would have been permanently frozen. When the climate ameliorated they would have thawed and become very soft and yielding and incapable of supporting fully the weight of the overlying sandstone which consequently bent down the slope and broke open along the joints. Cambering can be seen best at Bexley Hill. Here, Hythe Formation sandstones exposed in an old pit a little to the east of the road crossing the escarpment, 200 m or so back from the crest, display a regional dip of approximately 5° to the south. In contrast, blocks exposed along the sides of the road at the crest are approximately horizontal whilst just below the crest, dips are irregular but some exceed 10° down slope to the north.

The escarpments below the crest are also often stepped or the ground very irregular as a result of massive landslipping of the

© Ben du Boulay

The chert-reinforced sandstones in the Hythe Formation form high in-facing scarps overlooking the low ground of the Vale of Fernhurst, seen here at a distance from the east.

© David Robinson

Cemented sandstone beds of the Hythe Formation change dip and start to bend downslope due to cambering near the summit of Bexley Hill.

scarp face. This is very obvious at Older Hill and Bexley Hill on the southern scarp and at Blackdown on the northern. This landslipping may have originated at the same time and under similar conditions as the cambering. However, whilst cambering appears to be entirely inactive at the present day, some of the landslides remain unstable and further slippage still occurs, especially during wet winters and spring thaws. The largest is a massive rotational slip on the southwest face of Blackdown. It affects the entire depth of the scarp from 210 m to 90 m and extends for over 3 km. Above the road that today skirts the scarp is a steep upper slope, developed mostly in sandstones in the Hythe Formation, which is the degraded scar from where material has slipped down and out into the vale. Below is a complex mass of hummocky debris that stretches southwards, and merges over the gentler lower slopes with undulations associated with instability in the underlying Atherfield and Weald clays. Massive deep rotational sliding has affected the entire scarp, including these clays, which is evidenced by the back-tilted slope on the top of which stands Blackdown House over half a kilometre to the south. Similar massive slips have affected the east side of

Old photograph of the arcuate scar of the landslip at the western end of Older Hill descending towards Hookland and Redford.

The landslip scar at the western end of Older Hill today, exposing cemented sandstones and softer sands of the Hythe Formation.

© David Robinson

© David Robinson

Blackdown where Telegraph Cottage lies on a detached block of Hythe Formation sandstone that can be seen in a roadside exposure to the south to have a steep westward dip approaching 45°. Further north, subsidence of the Hythe sandstone beds has left a linear scar and terrace-like feature that runs for over 300 m just below the crest of the eastern slope with further landslipped masses below Aldworth House.

On the south side of the Vale of Fernhurst, similar ancient slips and cambered blocks can be inspected on the western side of Telegraph Hill, accessed via the minor road that terminates on Woolbeding Common before descending the scarp as a track. Older Hill, which is the highest point on a promontory running west from this track, lies 22 m below the summit of Telegraph Hill and is the first of a series of slipped, rotated blocks of the Hythe Formation that descend towards

Redford. The slope at the western end of this promontory remains unstable which is evidenced by a well-defined scar, largely hidden in woodland, that exposes up to 4 m or so of rubbly Hythe Formation sandstone above a steep slope overlooking Hookland. Hummocky ground created by other slips is widespread all along the wooded scarp and can be seen from footpaths and roads descending from Bexley Hill, Leggatt Hill, at Henley and below River.

Although fossil in origin, many of these landslips are not totally stable at the present day and further slippages sometimes occur in very wet winters. The problems are accentuated by water, passing into and through the porous and well-jointed Hythe Formation sandstones, emerging along the junction with the underlying impermeable Atherfield Clay and helping lubricate movement. In many places the junction is obscured by slipped material out of which the water seeps, but elsewhere there are a number of strong springs similar to those found at the foot of the Chalk. A good example emerges in the gardens of the Duke of Cumberland Inn at Henley.

The slightly higher areas of the floor of the Vale of Fernhurst are mostly covered by a layer of sand- and chert-rich rubble which overlies the underlying clay. Of variable thickness, the deposit is believed to be the remnants of freeze–thaw shattering of the sandstones in the Hythe Formation during the Quaternary, which descended the scarp and flowed out across the floor of the vale when it stood at a slightly higher level. Initially deposited as a continuous sheet or as lobes, subsequent erosion and incision by streams means that rem-

nants survive only on those areas of higher ground that have not been lowered by erosion. There are no good permanent exposures but stony, chert-rich fields can often be seen after ploughing.

The dip slopes of the porous sands and sandstones of the Hythe Formation are dissected by a series of dry valley systems similar to those on the Chalk, although many sustain variable spring-fed flows in their lower reaches. An excellent example is followed by the minor road running north from Easebourne to Bexley Hill. Springs that vary in activity according to weather conditions feed water into a stream that flows along the east side of the road and becomes a more permanent flow after crossing from the Hythe onto the less porous Sandgate Formation towards the bottom of the valley. On the northern outcrop the dip of the beds in the Hythe Formation is gentler and some of the extensive valley systems descending from Blackdown have cut through the higher beds of the Hythe Formation to the impervious Atherfield Clay below. Here water draining through the porous sandstones emerges along lines of springs that mark the junction between the two rock types.

© Ben du Boulay

The dip slopes of the Hythe Formation are dissected by valleys that lack streams in their upper reaches, but contain spring-fed streams lower down, such as the one channeled along the edge of the road at Easebourne which lies in the southern end of one of these valleys.

The River Rother, seen here in winter near Rogate, has excavated a large valley in weak silts and clays and in this part of Sussex has diverted all the drainage from the north to the east, to the River Arun.

The land sloping south from the Hythe Formation escarpment descends into the low-lying valley of the River Rother which is developed mostly in the rather poorly draining Sandgate Formation. The west–east flow of this river is a marked contrast to the predominantly north–south flow of the other major rivers crossing the Park. Whilst these south-flowing rivers are all thought to be quite ancient, originating probably as parts of the initial drainage system of the southern flank of the central dome of southeast England as it was uplifted, the western-flowing Rother is thought to have a more recent origin. Erosion of the dome would have been greatest along the line of greatest uplift across central Sussex and as the underlying rocks became exposed they exhibited a varying resistance to erosion. Surface-water flow and erosion became concentrated in areas of weak impervious clays and silts, along which tributary streams and rivers developed. The Rother is one of the principal examples of such a river, as are the east- and west-flowing sections of the Hammer Stream and River Lod that have hollowed out the Vale of Fernhurst. The westward development and the incision of the Rother along the easily eroded outcrop of the Sandgate Formation is believed to have captured the flow of rivers from the north that formerly flowed across the area at a high level and cut the notches in what is now the Chalk scarp to form the so called 'wind gaps'. If so, the depth of the valley below these gaps must have been excavated since this occurred. In more recent times, the incision of the Rother has in places left remnants of its former flat valley floor several metres above its present level. Separated from the present-day valley floor by a short steep slope, the relatively flat tops of these so-called 'terraces' are capped by rounded pebbles of flint and chert which can be seen exposed in places where the meandering present-day river is cutting into some of these terrace features as it continues to lower its valley.

Parts of the south-facing lower dip slope of the Hythe and the silt-rich Sandgate Formations are intensively cultivated and the light soils suffer from erosion. This is evidenced by quite significant differences, occasionally up to 1 metre or more, in the height of the ground surface on either side of hedges running across the slopes. This is because the hedges act as barriers to soil-laden water running off the fields, slowing down or ponding back the flow, which results in deposition of the eroded material. Some soil-laden water escapes through the hedges, and in particular through gateways, and after storm events the roads are often covered with significant quantities of either muddy water, or after drying with loose silty-sand. The area from Easebourne westwards, around Stedham, Trotton and Rogate, north of the A272, is particularly prone to this phenomenon.

On the south side of the Rother valley the land rises over the rather poorly drained silt-rich Sandgate Formation onto the free-draining sandy Folkestone Formation. These give rise to a series of raised,

© David Robinson

The outcrop of the sandy Folkstone Formation is marked by a series of wooded heathlands.

sometimes plateau-like heathlands that occasionally reach 75 m in the west, but mostly a height of 60–65 m. The heathlands are divided from each other by the valleys of tributary streams flowing northwards to join the Rother, from lower land under-

lain by Gault clay that lies further south. Several of the higher areas of the outcrop are capped by pale-coloured, angular flint gravels that must have come from the Chalk. Although once thought to be high-level river terrace deposits, the gravels are

© David Robinson

The flat-topped hills of the Folkstone Formation are frequently capped with a layer of broken angular flints that must have originated from the Chalk which today lies 2 km or so to the south. They are believed to be the remnants of vast sheets of frost-shattered material that spread out from the Downs when the land was at a higher level than today, probably in the penultimate cold period around 150,000 years ago. If this is correct, lowering of the intervening low ground must post-date their deposition.

now recognized as more likely the product of freeze–thaw action on the Chalk during cold periods in the Quaternary and to be the remnants of extensive sheets of material that spread out from the Downs when the land was at a higher level than today, probably in the penultimate cold period around 150,000 years ago. Since this time, erosion of the Gault that lies between the Chalk and the Folkestone Formation, has lowered much of the intervening land surface by 20–30 m. Some of these lower areas are overlain by later freeze–thaw deposits from the Chalk, known as 'head', that are less decalcified and contain larger, less bleached and shattered flint often intermixed with broken Chalk debris. Evidence suggests this material was deposited during the last cold period, particularly towards the end, in what is known as the late glacial, 13–10,000 years ago, when a marked oscillatory warming and cooling occurred. These deposits mostly occupy valleys within the Gault clay vale, and they can be traced back to small scallops or larger coombs in the Chalk scarp from where they originated, suggesting that the topography when they were deposited was not very different from that of the present day.

At the foot of the Downs, the Upper Greensand forms a distinct bench at the foot of the main Chalk escarpment. The bench is increasingly well developed westward and rises in height from the Arun to beyond Petersfield, where along with the other beds it swings north and reaches its maximal development around Selborne near the northern border of the Park. Here it forms an escarpment that reaches 175 m rising below the main Chalk scarp, whilst around Bignor and Sutton a little to the west of the Adur it reaches only 60–65 m. Looking east and southeast from the Upper Greensand escarpment near Selborne, or from the top of the Chalk scarp above, around Selborne Common there is an excellent view across the Gault clay vale to Woolmer Forest, located on the Folkestone Formation, and beyond, to the Hythe Formation sandstones dipping down from where they form the north rim of the Vale of Fernhurst. The scarp south of Selborne has suffered significant large-scale landslipping, which, as with slippage of the Hythe Formation sandstones, appears to date back to late glacial times and is today inactive except during very occasional wet periods when minor reactivation can occur.

The soils and land-use of the Western Weald

The contrasting and variable character of the rocks of the Lower Greensand gives rise to a complex of different soils, the properties of which depend on the relative proportions of sand, silt and clay within the geological parent material, and on their historic use by farmers. On the more silty and clay-rich members of the Sandgate and Hythe Formations, deep, rich, brown earth soils have developed. The clay content of these soils is sufficiently low for them to be generally free-draining, but they have poor structural stability and are therefore susceptible to erosion when cultivated. On the coarser, sandier and more silt-rich parent materials, more acidic, brown soils have developed with a lower base status and lower inherent fertility. Despite their relative infertility, these soils respond well to fertilizers and in some areas are valued for agriculture, particularly for fruit growing. Over the harder sandstones within the Hythe Formation, the soils are frequently thin, dry and stony. Most of these areas have remained uncultivated as common land or given over to forestry. Those under deciduous woodland tend to be markedly darker than those under cultivation, due to enrichment with humus from the decay of annual leaf litter.

Sand grains within these lighter soils are frequently bleached white due to the mobilization and removal of iron oxides. This marks the onset of what is referred to as podzolization, a process of degradation and depletion that reaches its full expression on the coarse sands of the Folkestone Formation. Here, the most degraded and infertile soils within the Park are found under the series of heathlands located adjacent to, and south of, the A272 from West Heath Common in the west to Washington Common in the east. They are the product both of the lack of nutrients and excessively free drainage of the underlying sands, and of their historic use first, for agriculture, which their low fertility could not sustain, and then as commons from which remaining nutrients were removed in the form of a variety of biological products such as turf, firewood, fodder, and animal bedding taken to support the local agricultural economy. Further degradation resulted from regular burning which limited the recycling of organic debris into the soil and a loss of volatile nutrients such as nitrogen.

The resulting soils, known as podzols, are up to a metre or more in depth and characterized by distinctly coloured layers or horizons with very different properties. The soil mineral surface is hidden by a matted layer of partially decomposed plant litter, below which lies a black humus-rich layer containing bleached sand grains. This is followed by a grey ash-coloured layer, which is frequently 50–75 cm deep. The bleached sand grains and ash colour are the result of washing by water, acidified as it passes down through the plant litter above, which flushes all humus, iron and any nutrients out of this part of the soil. The ash-coloured layer is terminated sharply at its base by a dark brown-black layer where humus carried from the upper soil, along with some iron and a few nutrients are redeposited. Sometimes the iron is redeposited as a thin, rust-brown cemented layer or 'pan' which, where well developed, may inhibit drainage. This may result in the development of a mixture of grey- and ochre-coloured mottles in the overlying layers. In free-draining soils, bands of further iron enrichment can often be detected in the underlying sands for a metre or more. The soils are acidic throughout and seriously deficient in nutrients. The extreme acidity excludes earthworms and restricts other soil fauna,

Heath scrub and woodland on Woolbeding Common is characteristic of the poor podzolic soils that develop on the high ground underlain by Hythe Formation sands and sandstones.

© Ben du Boulay

which partly explains the sharp boundaries between the different layers within the soils. Many good examples can be seen in roadside exposures and old sand-winning quarries.

In areas of poor drainage in hollows or adjacent to streams, downward flushing and drainage is limited. However, the acid conditions still mobilize the iron, but below the humus-enriched surface layer, the sub-surface layers are less clearly developed and grey-ochre mottling often predominates. In some very poorly drained boggy areas, such as on the lower areas of Ambersham Common, waterlogging so restricts the decay of dead plant material that peat forms on the surface whilst the underlying sands are bleached almost completely white. Peat accumulation is slow, and at the present day peat in valley bogs on the heathlands are all very thin. This is probably because accumulating peat was dug and used for fuel in former centuries.

© David Robinson

The profile of a podzol soil developed in the sands of the Folkestone Formation. The pale, ash-coloured, sub-surface horizon from which all iron and nutrients have been lost is the distinguishing feature of these soils.

In contrast, soils in those parts of the Park underlain by the impermeable Gault and Weald clays are heavy, poorly drained and waterlogged throughout most of the winter and early spring. The upper soil varies in colour from yellow to grey-brown, but below it is predominantly grey or blue-grey due to prevailing anaerobic conditions caused by waterlogging. Water frequently lies on the surface of the land during wet winter weather, but in hot summers the soils dry out, become hard and crack extensively. The soils are difficult to cultivate and traditionally large areas were under permanent grass that was often rich in wild flowers. In recent years, the introduction of underdraining has greatly extended the area regularly ploughed for arable cultivation or 'improved' grassland.

In conclusion

The landscape of the Park has been formed over many millions of years. As we have seen, most of the rocks were laid down over 70 million years ago, following which the structure was created by uplift associated with plate tectonics. After uplift, the actual landscape was created by differential erosion of rocks with varying properties and by re-deposition of some of the eroded residues. Elements of the landscape, such as the direction of the major north–south flowing rivers, are probably many millions of years old, but most features are much younger. Many major landscape features are largely fossil, created under climates that no longer prevail and by processes that are no longer very active at the present day. The deep permafrost and freeze–thaw related processes that operated during the Quaternary cold periods, the last of which ended only 10,000 years ago, have left a particularly strong imprint on the landscape. Associated sea-level changes have also had important impacts that continue to the present day.

Although many aspects of the landscape we see are inherited from the past they are nevertheless at the present day undergoing constant change. Rainfall and other climatic features weather the rocks and erode the landscape. Whilst many of these processes progress unnoticed and little may seem visibly to be changing, what are often considered exceptional events, associated with intense storms, exceptional rainfall, or exceptionally cold weather with severe freeze–thaw activity can have dramatic, newsworthy impacts. Within the area of the Park, large cliff falls, disruptive landslips, damaging river floods and severe soil erosion all occur several times in an average human life span, and this is a rapid frequency when considered on a geological time scale. All bear witness to the relatively rapid rate of continuing evolution of the landscape.

How to find out more about the geology and scenery of the South Downs National Park

If this introduction to the geology and scenery of the South Downs National Park has awakened interests that you wish to pursue further, then a selection of further reading is suggested (over the page), along with some websites that may be of interest. For those wishing to pursue an interest in geology, not just of the Downs, there are three very active geology societies in the region who are always pleased to welcome new members and run a variety of field excursions, including to RIGS (Regionally Important Geological Sites) and other sites not freely open to the public. These are: the Brighton and Hove Geological Society; the West Sussex Geological Society which is based in Worthing, and the Horsham Geological Field Club. All three maintain web sites that you can visit to find details. Details of RIGS sites are currently maintained on a county basis, most are within Sussex at the Sussex Biodiversity Records Centre, Woods Mill, Henfield. Contact: henribrocklebank@sussexwt.org.uk. Records are also available from the National Park Authority.

The National Park Authority is developing a variety of information resources, many of which are, or will shortly, be available online from their website, and downloadable in the field on the usual range of portable devices, as well as at home. They, the National Trust who own large tracts of the Park, and Local Authorities all run a variety of informed walks and excursions, often through their Ranger Services. Again, details are posted on their websites.

Throughout the book, emphasis has been on sites that can be visited or seen from roads, paths and bridleways within the Park, or lie within public access areas. A caution about visiting the cliffs is included in the text. When visiting these always be aware of the danger of falling rocks, preferably wear a hard hat, and when visiting any cliffs or shore platforms always ensure you know the tide times and allow plenty of time to safely reach access points.

Useful websites

www.bgs.ac.uk/ – Web site of the British Geological Survey giving access to maps, books and lots more both in electronic format and for purchase. Allows downloads to mobile devices but is not the easiest site to navigate!

Southdowns.gov.uk/ – Web site of the South Downs National Park Authority – and follow link to the learning zone where there is a section on Geology and Landscapes.

www.westsussexgeology.co.uk/ – The web site of a knowledgeable, enthusiastic local geologist David Bone who has information pages and runs field excursions.

www.ukfossils.co.uk/sussex.htm for those people interested in viewing and collecting fossils, including excursions.

If you would like to join a local geology society who have regular meetings and run excursions then look at the following:

www.wsgs.org.uk/ – Web site of the West Sussex Geological Society, based in Worthing.

www.bhgs.org/ – Web site of the Brighton and Hove Geological Society.

www.hgfc.uwclub.net – Web site of the Horsham Geological Field Club.

Further reading

Birch, R. 2006. *Sussex Stones – The Story of Horsham Stone and Sussex Marble.*

Castleden, R. 1996. *Classic Landforms of the Sussex Coast*, Geographical Association, Sheffield. (Covers sites within and outside the Park.)

Castleden, R. 2013. *The Sussex Coast: Land, Sea and the Geography of Hope.* Blatchington Press, Seaford. (A general text but with much relevant information on the National Park.)

Geographical Editorial Committee 1983. *Sussex: Environment, Landscape and Society*, Alan Sutton, Gloucester. (Includes slightly dated chapters on the geology, landforms, coast and soils of Sussex.)

Gibbons, W. 1981. *The Weald: A Geological Field Guide*, Unwin Paperbacks, London. (Includes an introduction to the geology of the Weald and geological excursions in the Park to Cow-Gap-Beachy Head, The Western Weald and Storrington.)

Larkin, M. and Vinyard, G. 2007. *In the Footsteps of Time: Geology and Landscape of Cuckmere Valley and Downs*, Ulmus Books.

Mitchell, C. 2004. *Landscape Walks in Sussex: Exploring the Geology of Sussex.*

Mortimore, R.N. 1997. *The Chalk of Sussex and Kent.* Geologists Association Guide 57, The Geologists Association, London. (An advanced text currently in the process of being revised.)

Robinson, D.A. and Williams, R.B.G. 1984. *Classic Landforms of the Weald*, Geographical Association, Sheffield. (Includes a chapter on the Vale of Fernhurst.)

Smart, G. and Brandon, P. (editors) 2007. *The Future of the South Downs*, Packard Publishing Limited, Chichester. (Includes a chapter on 'Rocks and Relief'.)

Geological Maps of the Downs are available online both in electronic and paper formats from the British Geological Survey website but the 1:50,000 are probably the most useful. Each map has a memoir, also available, that describes the geology of each sheet in detail. The sheets covering the National Park are: 299, 300, 301, 315, 316, 317, 318, 319, 333, 334.

And the relevant memoirs are:

Aldiss, D.T., Bristow, C.R., Chacksfield, B.C., Cornwell, J.D.C.D., Evans, R., Harris, P.M., Hobbs, P.R.N., Hobbs, S., Hopson, P.M. and Woods, M.A. 2002. *Geology of the Chichester and Bognor District: Sheet Description of the BGS 1:50,000 Series Sheet 317/332.* Nottingham. British Geological Survey.

Booth, K., Farrant, A., Hopson, P., Woods, M., Evans, D. and Wilkinson, I. 2008. *Geology of the Winchester District: Sheet Description of the British Geological Survey 1:50,000 Series Sheet 299 Winchester.* Nottingham. British Geological Survey.

Farrant, A.R., Hopson, P.M., Bristow, C.R., Westhead, R.K., Woods, M.A., Evans, D.J., Wilkinson, I.P. and Pedley, A. 2011. *Geology of the Alresford District: Sheet Description for the British Geological Survey 1:50,000 Series Sheet 300 Alresford (England and Wales).* Nottingham. British Geological Survey.

Gallois, R.W. and Worssom, B.C. 1993. *Geology of the Country Around Horsham: Memoir for 1:50,000 Geological Sheet 302 (England and Wales).* British Geological Survey. HMSO, London.

Hopson, P.N. 2000. *Geology of the Fareham and Portsmouth District: a Brief Explanation of the Geological Map Sheet 316 Fareham and Part of Sheet 331 Portsmouth.* Nottingham. British Geological Survey. HMSO, London.

Lake, R.D., Young, B., Wood, C.J. and Mortimore, R.N. 1987. *Geology of the Country around Lewes: Memoir for Geological Sheet 319.* British Geological Survey. HMSO, London.

Thurrell, R.G., Worssam, B.C. and Edmonds, E.A. 1968. *Geology of the Country around Haslemere.* Institute of Geological Sciences (Great Britain). HMSO, London.

Young, B. and Lake R.D. 1988. *Geology of the Country around Brighton and Worthing. Memoir for Geological Sheets 318 and 333.* British Geological Survey. HMSO, London.

Index of locations and sites